Matthias
Willenbacher

My
indecent
PROPOSAL

to the
GERMAN
CHANCELLOR

Because we cannot let the ENERGY TRANSITION fail!

The original German version was published by
Verlag Herder GmbH, Freiburg im Breisgau/Germany

Jacket theme: Carina Jahn, Wiesbaden (www.carina-jahn.de)

Jacket design: Performers GmbH, Wiesbaden (www.performers.de)
Typesetting & Production: Performers GmbH, Wiesbaden

Editors: Lars Jansen, Bad Berleburg (www.lektorat-jansen.de)

Translation, updating and editing: Dieter Wermuth, Ph.D., Mainz

Printed on eco-friendly, chlorine-free bleached paper

Printed in Germany

ISBN 978-3-00-046160-6

2nd, revised edition

The book online:
www.my-indecent-proposal.com

Preface

When I first came across Matthias Willenbacher's book one year ago, I could not stop reading. It's a rags-to-riches story of an entrepreneur with a message: the destruction of the environment must end. Matthias is one of the drivers of Germany's Energiewende which has created a new and fast-growing industry—the generation of energy from wind, sun and biomass. Renewables already account for one quarter of the country's electricity production and have become a major job machine. The new technologies herald the end of the carbon economy. It is not that we run out of oil—just as the stone age did not come to an end because we ran out of stones. Investors should not bet on fossil fuels anymore.

Matthias Willenbacher makes an offer: if, by 2020, all electricity comes from renewables, he will give his shares in project developer juwi AG to the one thousand or so energy cooperatives which are the grassroots promoters of renewables (p. 54).

That the transition can be achieved in such a short time is the book's main theme. But politicians, under pressure from "old energy", have recently decided to slow down the Energiewende and reduce the subsidies for renewables. The good news, however, is that the cost of solar power is falling dramatically (p. 61)—in Germany today, one kwh of electricity can already be produced for 6 cents. Wind power is also getting cheaper. Renewables are quickly becoming competitive without subsidies. At the same time, the demand for clean energy is bound to increase, as the destruction of the world's environment continues to this day (p. 89). Forecasts of fossil fuel consumption based on past trends will be wrong. We are approaching a phase change. Matthias' 100-per cent goal may still be reached, simply thanks to market forces.

Given the importance of this book for mankind—as well as the investment community—I gladly helped to translate and update Matthias' book.

Dieter Wermuth
Mainz, July 2014

Dedication

I dedicate this book to my parents. They gave me the strength, the will and the determination to go my way. They taught me how to devote my full energy to a good cause.

The thought that my father will not be able to read this book makes me sad. He supported my projects with all his heart until his death in January 2013.

My mother has not only recently lost her husband—several years ago, both her daughters died. I hope to give back to her a little bit of all the good she has given me.

Two other important people have supported, accompanied and stood by me in the past decades: my brother Norbert as well as my partner and friend, Fred Jung. Without my brother, I would not have made it, and without the "ju" there would not have been the "wi" in juwi, our firm.

Contents

Foreword: My indecent proposal

I grew up on a farm in the northern Pfalz region of Germany, 100 kilometers southwest of Frankfurt. My original goal in life was to work as little as possible. Today, I am a workaholic and manage a billion euro company with subsidiaries in many countries around the globe.

I am grateful that I made it from farm boy to co-founder and co-chief executive of juwi. But that is not the reason I wrote this book.

I built a wind turbine twenty years ago on my parents' farm. A large renewable energy firm has developed from those early experiments, and it has given meaning to my life. I would like to contribute as much as I can to ensure that we switch from the production of dirty, import-dependent, environmentally destructive and expensive energy to clean and sustainable energy.

I do not want to proselytize, and I also do not want to present myself as a do-gooder. My aim is to explain what I, as an entrepreneur and citizen, have experienced in developing renewable energy. And I want to provide information that helps people to make decisions about the way energy is produced in the future.

I am sure that the rapid switch to 100 per cent clean and locally generated energy is the best solution for all of us. Many politicians shake their heads and say that it will never work.

The attitude of these people has been a recurring feature in my whole professional life. My first wind mill: I was a student, needed one million Deutschmarks to construct it—and everyone threw wrenches into my wheels. At my company I started as my own cleaning lady and switch board operator—today we have 1,600 employees. My experience with politics: I have been told for decades that electricity generated from wind and sun was a pipedream and would never work.

I did it anyway, despite many obstacles. Renewables do, in fact, work. Overcoming skepticism and obstacles leaves a lasting impression. I am convinced that we can completely switch to renewable energy

by 2020—sustainably, decentralized and affordably. It is not impossible. We can do it if we all pull together.
But we need someone to lead the way. That person is our chancellor Angela Merkel.
That is why I am making her an "indecent" proposal.
Don't worry, I will not try to pay her a bribe. But I am willing to give everything that I have built.
More precisely, I will donate all shares in my company, juwi AG, if the chancellor realizes the energy transition, the famous "Energiewende", in full, by 2020, without any ifs and buts. Here and now.
One might say that the proposal itself is indecent—because there is no risk that it can be realized. But that is exactly my point: it can!
The chancellor should take the lead. She has called preventing a climate catastrophe "the biggest challenge of the twenty first century". The German Energiewende can serve as a role model for the rest of the world. The federal government can pave the way for the 100 per cent energy transition. The German parliament can decide that we will generate all our energy from clean and decentralized sources by 2020. Angela Merkel and Sigmar Gabriel, her new "Super"-Minister of the Economy and Energy, can make it happen.
Long-term, the immediate and complete Energiewende is better and more cost-efficient for everyone if we, the citizens, are driving it forward. Let's end our dependence on the large players in energy production. Once we are in charge, the profits will no longer go to just a few companies, but to all of us.
We should all become "energy citizens". That is what it is all about. If the German chancellor accepts my offer, I will give my shares in juwi AG to the country's more than 900 energy cooperatives. They all participate in wind and solar projects and are the basis of our future energy supply. My dream can come true if they support me in my fight for the immediate and complete energy transition. Help me—and all of us—by writing letters to the chancellor.

1

The Energiewende is failing. Now what?

The night of Fukushima

On Saturday night 12 March 2011, I did not sleep. I was hooked to my TV and smartphone. I watched the reports to find out what happened in Fukushima in the wake of the most powerful earthquake in recent Japanese history and a tsunami which had hit the main island at 3:36 PM local time (7:36 AM CET). This had caused an explosion at the Fukushima-Daiichi nuclear power plant. Several reactor units were severely damaged, including core meltdowns and a release of radioactivity.
I felt deep sorrow. What a disaster for nature and the Japanese people! And I asked myself: What does this mean? In the weeks that followed I became increasingly confident that this time we would learn from the event and make decisive changes.

According to the propaganda from the nuclear energy lobby, an accident of this kind is only expected every 500,000 years. Strange then that a few years after Chernobyl, a second major disaster has occurred.

It had only been four months after Merkel's conservative-liberal coalition government had decided to abandon the nuclear phase-out and to extend the life of the seventeen German nuclear power plants. That was a shining moment for Germany's nuclear and coal-powered electricity companies. "Germany's dark power", as stern.de wrote back then, had shown who really had the say in our country, who was in charge of energy politics. And who submissively lobbied for them. Especially since the free market-FDP (German Liberals) had been part of the government.

But now Länder (state) elections were coming up in March 2011 in Baden-Württemberg and Rheinland-Pfalz (Rhineland-Palatinate), home of juwi and myself. In the days after the catastrophe, I watched very closely how these horrible events in far-away Japan were communicated by the German media. There were suddenly no longer two opposing views, only one: get out of nuclear power immediately! In Ms Merkel's CDU (Christian Democratic Union), even hardcore nuclear power advocates who had always spoken of an insignificant "remaining risk", quickly became advocates of a nuclear power phase-out. Only the leading Rheinland-Pfalz FDP politician, Rainer Brüderle, state minister for the economy at the time, begged to differ. As he explained to the top-managers of German industry, among them the CEOs of Eon and RWE, the giant utilities, the government was under great pressure ahead of the two state elections and could not act as rationally as it should. He, however, remained an advocate of nuclear power.

The FDP then lost the state elections and was booted out of parliament in Mainz. The Bündnis 90/Die Grünen (The Greens), with 15 per cent of the vote, made it back into the state chamber and joined the SPD (Social Democrats) in the new government. In Baden-Württemberg, the CDU, a traditional supporter of nuclear power, was kicked-out of power, after 58 years. State premier Stefan Mappus lost his job. The Greens formed a coalition government with the Social Democrats. For the first time ever, a member of the Greens (Winfried Kretschmann) was heading a state government.

After the overwhelming success of the green candidates, the federal government repealed its 2009 decision to keep the nuclear power plants running for a long time. Now the reactors were to be phased out by 2022. No one had any doubts that the Energiewende would succeed.

How the Energiewende lost its momentum

As sad as the event was that triggered all this, there was clearly a sense of change in the air. Mayors, county administrators and energy cooperatives took the words of politicians as an unambiguous signal that they should and could now invest in renewable energy. And they did just that. This created a tremendous momentum. Many energy projects were launched. I remember that practically everybody told me the same: "Hey, Matthias, it's starting. The Energiewende is for real. Now the direction is finally clear."

Today, nothing is clear anymore.

Today, we must ask ourselves: how can we save the Energiewende? It can fail dramatically or become an unprecedented success story— depending on what politicians do and what we as a society want. On the first anniversary of Fukushima, the former Minister for the Environment, Klaus Töpfer, complained that both—the government and the civil service—were lacking enthusiasm, in contrast to the general population. That is putting it politely. It is unbelievable how poorly German politicians are managing today's most important project.

Merkel's nuclear power phase-out just re-established what the SPD-Green coalition government had decided in 2000. This decision had been reversed by the conservative-liberal coalition in 2009: nuclear power plants were given an extension. Several of the nine nuclear power stations still running today were allowed to operate until 2022. By then, their electricity output should be completely replaced by other forms of energy generation.

The nuclear power phase-out is not the same as the Energiewende. The Merkel government did not change the goals for renewable energy: its share in electricity generation is to increase to 35 per cent by 2020. The only thing that was added in 2009 were the words "at least"—"to at least 35 per cent".

A study commissioned by the German Association for Renewable Energy showed that a share of 47 per cent would be quite feasible. The Berlin government had always justified the extension of the nuclear plants' life on the basis of a paper that claimed the development of renewable energy was not fast enough—nuclear power was needed as a "bridge". To me, this was just an excuse. It would have been no problem at all to accelerate the development of renewables. Politicians could have aimed for 45 per cent by 2020, rather than 35 per cent. But they didn't.

As it is, the transition from fossil fuels to renewables is supposed to take until the middle of this century—36 years! Even then, renewables are scheduled to account for only 80 per cent of electricity output. That is important to know. It is clear that the Merkel government was never really convinced of the project from the beginning, despite all the declarations to the contrary.

This mindset is reflected in the section on energy policies in the contract between the conservatives and Social Democrats which is the blueprint of the new federal government's projects for the four years until 2017. The paper on the so-called corner points of the coming reform of the law on renewable energies (EEG) was even more skeptical: it was presented by „super minister" Gabriel in mid-February 2014. If the proposals in these documents were fully implemented, the Energiewende would be more or less dead. Even though it appears likely that Mr Gabriel will agree to some small changes, firms in the renewable energy sector are highly concerned and irritated. Capital expenditures and projects are put on hold, many jobs for innovative and highly-skilled workers are at risk.

Politicians of all German parties continue to claim they want the Energiewende. Perhaps that is true for many of them, including members of the new government. But they are lacking the will, the power and perhaps also the competence to really advance the transition to renewable energy. The few but powerful opponents of the energy transition certainly do not lack such expertise—and they are hell-bent on delaying it for as long as possible. And they have learned the business of distraction, confusion, fear, obviation and blocking from bottom up. You have to give them credit for that.

I have experienced it myself since the middle of the 90s.

And it has been more of the same in the years since Fukushima.

The strategies of old energy

Once it was clear that the phase-out of nuclear power could not be stopped any longer—at least for the time being—strings were pulled in the background to slow down the Energiewende. Hidden from the public, facts were created: German coal-burning power plants may now operate beyond the year 2050. Global warming from this source will thus continue to accelerate. What the old energy producers are doing makes financial sense. The problem is that they are not admitting openly that they are mainly interested in profits. So they come through the back door, often exploiting citizens' initiatives for their aims.

For years now, especially after Fukushima, the established utilities are making the same claims. Their interest is to keep the fossil fuel regime in place. They argue:

1. renewable electricity is too expensive for the consumer;
2. the German economy will become less competitive because renewables drive up the cost of energy;
3. without nuclear power and coal, there will be blackouts and supply shortages;
4. there is a lack of storage facilities: we must wait until these are in place;
5. the Energiewende requires offshore wind parks.

At some point people would be so scared by the risks that they would resign and say "Let's just leave things as they are." This is what the electricity oligopolists are betting on. If the strategy is successful, we would be tumbling, eyes wide open, toward climate catastrophes, energy wars, and collapsing economies and societies—and only because clean energy is not yet taken seriously as a viable alternative to electricity from nuclear and fossil fuels.

Already in 2009, Stephan Kohler, director of the German Energy Agency (dena), had asserted a shortage of electricity supply. In the summer of 2011, after seven nuclear power plants had been shut down, many so-called experts predicted fatal electricity shortages and blackouts. It did not happen.

So they had to change their strategy and came up, in early 2012, with a new argument: the shut-down of nuclear power plants requires new coal burning power plants—and this would harm the climate even more than nuclear power.

As it happened, the shut-down of the nuclear power plants was easily compensated by the rapid growth of renewables. Since an "electricity gap" did not materialize after all, the established utilities switched to the argument that pushing ahead with renewables would make electricity too expensive.

That is the current state of things.

What's wrong with the Renewable Energies Act (EEG) and the EEG levy

Peter Altmaier (CDU), the former Minister for the Environment, has invented a euphemism—the "electricity price brake". I regard it as another attempt to slow the growth of renewables in favor of supposedly "inexpensive" electricity from coal. The EEG levy was presented as the main culprit for the increase of households' electricity bills, and in fact as the price for the Energiewende! Ever since that time there is a public discussion whether households and businesses pay too much for electricity—because of the EEG levy. As of January 2014, it is 6.24 cents per kilowatt hour, up 18.3 per cent from 2013. It is charged by the operators of the electricity grid and is used to finance a part of the subsidies for renewables.

Politicians are trying to hide the fact that electricity prices are rising for other reasons as well. Altmaier's intention to cap or freeze the EEG-levy could not succeed: the price for the purchase of green electricity is regulated (and fixed) by law. At the same time, the price at the electricity exchange is not fixed—it responds to changes in demand and supply. When it falls, the EEG levy rises automatically (ie, beyond 6.24 cents): the producers of green energy get the same price no matter what.

The actual EEG-levy is the difference between the politically fixed renewable energy feed-in tariff and the spot price at the electricity exchange. The feed-in tariff is assumed to be the price at which operators have an incentive to install capacities which produce clean energy. From this, the price at the electricity exchange is deducted. In other words: the lower the spot price of electricity at the exchange, the higher the EEG-levy!!

Consumers should benefit from falling prices at the electricity exchange, but don't.

This is exactly what is wrong about the system. The large power utilities do not pass on their savings—they rather prefer to boost their earnings. This means that households subsidize the four oligopolists and the producers of old energy in general—they also subsidize energy-intensive manufacturers. These are serious distortions of the German economy. They are also a brake on medium-term GDP growth.

In this book I ask the question: is the EEG-levy the right price to focus on? And even if the answer is yes: should the further expansion of renewable energy depend on this?

Household electricity price vs. spot market price 2000–2013

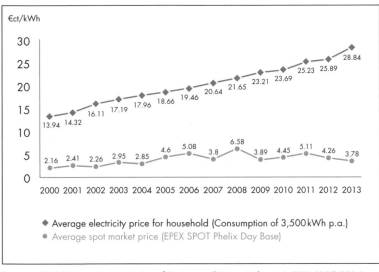

Sources: BDEW (German Association of Energy and Water Industries), EPEX SPOT 2014

If you take a closer look at the additional costs that households have to shoulder to promote renewable energy, a further question arises: how relevant are these costs for people's standard of living? Take for example a family which consumes 4,000 kilowatt hours of electricity per year; for this it pays about 1,000 euros; for heating and driving a car, the average household spends about 4,000 euros—for a total of 5,000 euros. The EEG-levy is about 250 euros, or 5 per cent of 5,000 euros, the annual amount of money needed for electricity, heating and mobility. For 250 euros you can fill up your car two or three times.

From a strictly economic point of view, the EEG-levy cannot be the main problem. I therefore wonder why we are discussing it so intensely and emotionally. The relevant question is how to reduce the rest of households' expenditures: 4,750 euros is a much larger burden than those 250 euros. Of course, there are families who really hurt by rising electricity prices. But the increase of oil and gas prices is an even bigger problem for them.

The FDP (the liberals) and long-term unemployment benefits (Hartz-IV)

Let me say a few words about the FDP, the minority partner in the second Merkel coalition government. The party was kicked out of the federal parliament on September 22, 2013 and has been replaced by Social Democrats in Merkel's third (4-year) government. When electricity prices became a hot topic, the FDP suddenly discovered the poor "Hartz-IV" recipients who had previously not been famous for being members of the FDP constituency. The party had mostly appealed to farmers, professionals, small business, hotel owners (!), civil servants and generally to people who felt they were paying too much tax. The FDP had also fought aggressively, and very successfully, for the interests of energy-intensive companies. These are largely exempted from the EEG-levy. Many other firms had been exempted from the EEG-levy as well by the previous parliament. Consumers had to pick up the bill. No wonder they became so angry about the cost of electricity.

The exceptions were originally only meant for energy-intensive companies who are competing internationally. How come the German Weather Service or lignite miners were exempted from the levy as well? A giant brown coal excavator consumes as much electricity as a small town. Why should they benefit from subsidized electricity prices? After all, they destroy both the landscape and the climate, they do not contribute to the costs of developing clean energy, and they have little incentive to improve their energy efficiency.

The rationale of the exemptions escapes me. And I cannot understand why people who live on welfare (Hartz-IV) have to pay the full levy. They don't get any subsidy! In public speeches, improving the life of the poor had been the top priority of almost all politicians. How hypocritical can you get?

Why didn't the FDP promote the Energiewende? On the one hand, the party tried to appeal to those who are opposed to the concept as such. On the other hand, the party has traditionally railed against centrally planned economies. For the FDP, the Energiewende was a prime example of such "communist" policies. It thus became the voice of the big players in the energy sector.

Why are coal-burning power plants considered to be financially viable?

Why are the utilities' coal-burning power plants currently "financially viable"? One reason is that the price of coal has fallen a lot, not least because of the shale gas and shale oil revolution in the US. There is now an oversupply of coal.

Steam coal—German average import prices

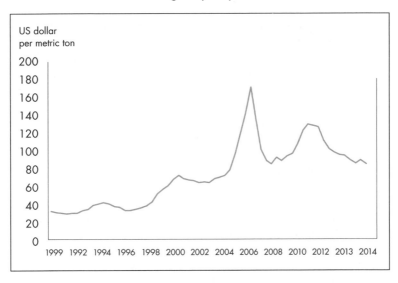

US dollar
per metric ton

Sources: Bundesamt für Wirtschaft und Ausfuhrkontrolle; own calculations

The second reason is the failure of the market for CO_2-certificates. Under pressure from lobbies in Brussels, far too many certificates had been issued—which continues to depress their market price. The enormous environmental damage caused by burning coal is not at all reflected in the price of electricity. This, incidentally, makes electricity from gas relatively expensive and thus causes an under-investment in gas-fired power stations. This is a shame because they are an indispensable part of the Energiewende. Also, the so-called electricity price brake is nothing other than an attempt to discour-age decentralized "grass-roots" energy production in favor of the large power utilities. Altmaier, the former CDU minister for environmental issues, had hoped to win votes with his price brake, but in effect, he was just promoting the interests of "old energy" rather than the Energiewende.

To slow the transition to renewables is like saying, after the invention of the computer, that we should continue using typewriters during a transitory phase—until everybody had a computer. Or that we should use smoke signals for another 30 years to communicate, until everybody had access to a telephone; or, in the 90's, wait before switching from fixed line telephones to mobiles.

Making phone calls with cell phones has become dramatically less expensive within just a few years—as the technology has improved enormously. The same will happen to renewables. The process is already under way. But no one is talking about that. Photovoltaics is an example for large technological advances and impressive cost reductions. As it was, Ms Merkel's conservative-liberal government drastically reduced feed-in tariffs in 2011 and especially in 2012. The policy ruined the image of the industry and its international competitiveness.

Why the enthusiasm for wind power at sea?

The usual opponents of renewable energy make one exception: offshore wind. Instead of quickly building decentralized power plants using renewables, close to where the electricity is needed, giant and expensive offshore wind parks are being created in the north, far away from consumers, mostly for the industry in the south of Germany. This requires new high-voltage lines across the country and a lot of time and money. The result: the Energiewende will be significantly delayed and become unnecessarily expensive.

When the planning of offshore parks began, the assumptions were that there would not be enough onshore wind and that the electricity from sea wind would be inexpensive. Both assumptions have long shown to be wrong. So why is expensive offshore electricity still an issue given that onshore wind mills are substantially less expensive? Because offshore is where the large utilities will be able to dominate the business, subsidized by the government. They expect billion-euro profits. Small investors are effectively excluded. The concept of the Energiewende is radically different: it is bottom-up! It is about small and mid-sized power generators, communities and cooperatives, not about the big boys.

The 2013 Bundestag election and the Energiewende

It is important that the transition to renewables is properly implemented—our survival depends on it. It determines whether there will be a life worth living on this planet— now and for generations to come. All over the globe crucial decisions are delayed all the time while the gradual deterioration of the environment continues. People must therefore take matters into their own hands.

In Germany, the federal elections of September 22, 2013 had been an opportunity to do this. Somehow the two largest parties, the conservative CDU/CSU and the center left Social Democrats, succeeded to keep environmental issues off the table during the campaign. They argued that things were on the right track, Germany was actually a role model for the world in terms of Energiewende, and that it was about time to slow and adjust the process. Much had gone wrong. In particular, electricity prices paid by households had increased too quickly. The term "Energiewende" had become a negative term for many, thanks to the never-ending stream of scare scenarios produced by the friends of big energy. It was no longer clear to everybody that the energy transition was a promise and a path to a better future.

The election results were a shock for environmentalists. Ms. Merkel's conservatives overwhelmingly won, with 41.5 per cent of the vote; the Social Democrats shrank to 25.7 per cent, and the Greens to 8.4 per cent, down from 10.7 per cent in 2009. The "Linke" (the Left) dropped to 8.6 per cent while the FDP, the "liberal" supporter of the big energy producers, did not pass the 5-per cent threshold and was therefore eliminated from parliament.

For the third time in post-war Germany, a grand coalition took over the government. The two possible alternatives were politically not yet feasible: the conservatives were not willing for compromises with the Greens, while the Social Democrats were afraid to cooperate with the supposedly communist Left. Of the 630 seats in the Bundestag, the lower house of parliament in Berlin, the CDU/CSU got 311, the SPD 192, for a total of 503 seats—or almost 80 per cent. The opposition is now so small they cannot claim chairmanships of law-making committees.

I am afraid that the advocates of big energy have won an important battle against those who had fought for a decentralized system where decisions are made by citizens and local communities. The conservatives want market forces to drive the development of renewables, provide additional support for energy-intensive firms, construct new grids and storage facilities, build gas and coal power plants and have another look at fracking.

Sigmar Gabriel, the leader of the Social Democratic Party (SPD), became vice chancellor and minister for the economy and energy, a new power center. In the previous (2005 to 2009) grand coalition he had been minister for the environment. The SPD wants to keep the guarantees for the feed-in of electricity from renewables, intends to lower the levy for subsidizing renewables, and is in favor of new gas and coal power plants—but against fracking. At least for now.

In other words, the new government wants to pursue the Energiewende, but at a much slower pace. I am afraid that Frau Merkel is not about to accept my offer to hand over my shares in juwi AG to energy cooperatives if 100 per cent of all electricity comes from renewables by 2020.

"Energiewende"—the eyes of the world are on Germany

The term "Energiewende"—energy transition—was first coined in 1980 in a study of the Ecological Institute of Freiburg, Germany; it was not widely used by the general public.

In the meantime, the word has a broader meaning than just the phase-out of nuclear energy and the reorganization of the electricity industry. It means, first of all, the shift away from oil, coal, gas and uranium toward sustainable and renewable energies for electricity, heat and mobility. These include wind and sun, but also biomass, hydropower and geothermal energy.

But the Energiewende is not only a technological or economic concept. Perhaps even more importantly, it is a social, cultural and, fundamentally, also a humanistic idea about our society's future.

Today, the word Energiewende is used all over the globe. The eyes of the world are on Germany: will we be able to achieve the transition? Whether we want it or not, we are regarded as a role model. If we end up as a misguided pioneer the rest of the world may conclude that the "Energiewende didn't work. Let's just forget it".

Germany is the planet's laboratory. We may prove that the switch to renewables can be a social, environmental and, last but not least, an economic success.

Since 2011, the representatives of big energy as well as many government officials have portrayed the Energiewende as a threat. This is how they argue: we may heat up the planet by less and avoid nuclear catastrophes like Chernobyl and Fukushima if we stop burning coal and using uranium—this we admit—but electricity will become so expensive that our economy will collapse. It is then back to the caves!

In my opinion, it is exactly the other way round: the Energiewende will make electricity more affordable while the demand for the increasingly expensive fossil fuels will decline. Our economy can experience another golden era, and we can maintain today's prosperity. The Energiewende will make sure that our children and grandchildren will not be worse off.

Rather than a threat the Energiewende is the road into a bright future. Many local communities, counties and energy cooperatives have successfully been implementing it—and it works! You just have to know where to look.

The problem and its solution—in a few sentences

We need a society which enthusiastically supports the Energiewende. Only then can we stand up to the interests of the established electricity providers, their propaganda and threats. We need positive emotions to fill its promise with life.

Our prosperity is based on seemingly inexpensive fossil fuels. The consequences have been ignored for a long time. Such an approach will no longer work.

Two sentences suffice to explain why that is so:

– Fossil fuels are finite and increasingly expensive.

– Fossil fuels cause and accelerate the greenhouse effect.

What now?

One sentence will actually do: renewable energies are the solution for both problems.

There are most certainly serious challenges along the way. Above all, people must make decisions for or against certain projects. They have to insist that they want to be involved. If they do not agree, nothing goes, for instance whether, and why, we need new giant power lines. The more decentralized the Energiewende and the more ordinary citizens are involved, the less likely is it that such electricity corridors will be needed.

In this book, I deal with the arguments of the opposition in a comprehensive way. Are renewables expanding too fast? How does the Energiewende relate to the issues of electricity prices and social fairness? Does the energy transition endanger Germany's industrial competitiveness, will it lead to de-industrialization? Will renewables cause brownouts and power failures? I will describe in detail how a 100% switch to renewables can work. I will map out the path to the future, how tapping the power of sun and wind raises global living standards and fairness, and how, above all, it would transform societies.

Energiewende or chicory?

In early 2013 I had an experience which is not much different from the ones I had in the one and a half decades before: it is difficult to speak with certain politicians about the Energiewende.
I had accompanied Angela Merkel, the chancellor, on her trip to Chile. I was there as a business representative of the renewable energy sector.
On the flight back from Chile to Germany Ms. Merkel wanted to drink a glass of wine with the six businessmen onboard. She spoke about Argentina's president Kirchner, Kuba's Raul Castro and Bolivia's president Evo Morales.
We had only been in the air for about two hours at the time and had another 13 hours to go. We had enough time, and so I wanted to take the opportunity to speak with her about the Energiewende. Before the trip, she had given a speech about wind power in the north of Germany, and I wanted to discuss that with her. Therefore, I asked her: "Could we perhaps speak about the Energiewende for a few minutes? I have some questions and a few ideas"
She looked at me and simply said: "Write me a letter."
I would be lying if I did not admit that I was somewhat irritated and disappointed as we went back to our seats. Next to me sat a representative from Südzucker, the large sugar producer. Merkel had asked him the same question she asked the rest of us: what was he doing in Chile? He said his company grew chicory in order to produce fructose from it.
All of a sudden I saw how Merkel walked down the aisle and came toward me. She actually stopped at my seat. I thought: Well this is nice. She's thought about it and wants to speak with me about the Energiewende after all! But no, she just leaned over me and told the man from Südzucker that she was planning to prepare a chicory dish—and whether he might have a few tips for her.
I thought: ok. She has other priorities.
The chancellor discussing the preparation of chicory!

Her sentence "Write me a letter" wouldn't get out of my mind.

At that moment I decided: Yes, I will write.

But not a letter, I will write a book.

I have no idea whether it is good or bad that I write here about my brief encounter with the chancellor. Perhaps I will not get invited any more. Perhaps I am harming my company. As it is, the issue is simply too important for me. I have to talk about the episode. Without it, this book would not have been written.

Because the Energiewende must succeed. We cannot let it fail because some politicians are opposed, or because it reduces the profitability of big energy. We are at a crossroads. We can continue to ruin the environment and enrich the producers of fossil fuels. This is not what I want. Let us opt for a future of safe, independent, sustainable and affordable energy.

Energy issues must move up on the public's priority list; they are more than the private business of a few large companies. Even some Greens are saying that we need the cooperation between utilities, coal producers and the people. That is a nice thought, but the reality is different. The old system of coal companies and a few nationwide electricity producers is not compatible with the new decentralized system where local communities and households make the decisions. It is either one or the other.

We need a new era of participation and democracy.

We need an Energiewende driven by you and me.

And we need it now.

2

The first wind turbine

How a newspaper article changed my life

I still cannot explain why exactly a newspaper article has changed my life. It was not even on the first page, but somewhere in the regional news section in the back. And I only read it because I was in hospital, was bored and did not know what else to do.

But perhaps I should tell my story from the beginning, though not exactly from my birth on July 14, 1969. I grew up on a farm in Schneebergerhof, a hamlet of 80 residents, 60 kilometers (37 miles) southwest of Mainz, the capital of Rheinland-Pfalz, one of Germany's 16 "Länder" (states). The hilly area were we lived has been called "Siberian Pfalz" in the popular TV crime series "Tatort" (crime scene). In the meantime, the population of the village has shrunk to about 40! My parents, Hans and Irene Willenbacher, were full-time farmers. I have a brother, Norbert, who is almost ten years older than I. He is currently a physics professor at the University of Karlsruhe. The most important person for me as a child was one of my sisters. But she died in a car accident when I was eleven.

After my brother got married in his mid-twenties, I was alone on the farm helping my parents. We had 20 cows, which was quite a large number back then. The smaller farms in the area had only three or four. Very few farms had 50 or more. We also had 60 pigs, a few chickens, cats and mice.

That means my parents were in the stable 365 days a year. After homework, I had to help out—and from morning to evening during vacation time. Winter break, Easter break, summer vacation, and fall break—I rarely had any time off. I know that I had been at summer camps in Austria when I was eleven to thirteen years old, but I never had vacations with my parents. During summer breaks, work usually began at six in the morning and did not end before midnight. I learned then what it means to be available at all times, and to work non-stop. While cleaning the cots, hacking beets or driving the tractor I told myself that I would not do this as an adult. My parents wanted one of their sons to take over the farm. It was clear to me from early on that I would not be the one.

I took the primary school entrance exam twice. It was somehow too boring for me the first time. When I finally passed the test, the teacher said to my mother: "Your older son has been a very good student, your daughter also—but your youngest!!! Well, there is a black sheep in just about every family." I remember the sentences to this day even though I was only five years old at the time. My brother was attending high school ("Gymnasium") and was always top of the class there. I did not do quite so well but I was also a fairly good student, especially in math and science.

Nevertheless, my school career was not impressive. The primary school years were ok—as far as I can remember –, but high school had not been a big success. The fact that I, as a farmer's son, was going for the Abitur (German high school exam, after 4 plus 9 years of school) was ok for my parents. But I did not attend the same high school as my primary school classmates. I went to a Gymnasium in Kirchheimbolanden because my brother and my cousin had both graduated from there. At the age of ten, you didn't really question things like that. At the high school in nearby Winnweiler, most of the kids were like me, from farming families, whereas in my high school, the children's parents were business people, civil servants and professionals. It was not easy to be one of the few farm boys in class. First of all, I was almost a year younger than most and one of the smallest. And I wore hand-knitted sweaters and had a bowl cut. And so I was initially an outsider in my class. Not until my height was close to average did my situation improve. But I never developed any real friendships. After graduation, I quickly lost contact to most of my classmates.

In the beginning, I took the school bus shortly after 6:00 a.m. The school was actually only 18 kilometers (11 miles) away, but the bus took a longer route and I had to change to another one in between. So I was traveling for almost two hours every morning and again one and a half hours in the afternoon. During the school holidays and breaks, it was not much better. When the others were rolling out of bed at ten, I was already up and working for two or three hours. I was busy doing farm work about 50 to 60 hours a week. This was normal for me.

Finally free: university in Mainz

When I moved from Schneebergerhof to the big wide world, to study physics in Mainz, the first thing I heard from my professors was: "Matthias, please speak proper German, not dialect."
I thought: what?
But my fellow students at the Johannes Gutenberg University also did not understand me.
I adjusted very quickly because I did not want to be an outsider again. It may sound strange, but I had to get used to waking up later in the morning. I actually had to learn how to remain in bed after partying the night before. As it was, I adjusted rather quickly. In 1991 I had almost six months off. The semester had ended in mid-June. I spent my time swimming and traveling with friends through Europe on an InterRail pass. When I returned at the end of September, my vacation job at the university was gone because the professor had suddenly died. It was the longest phase in my life without work, and it has remained so until this day. In 1993, I was still the youngest in my physics graduation class. I had just turned 24.
The next step would have been my doctorate. But I was no longer interested in physics. The subject was not difficult, it was just that the work seemed very theoretical. I could not figure out what to do with it in real life. Today, I am aware that the main reason I had chosen physics was my brother—he had been my role model and I didn't know better. At the end of 1991, I had begun to study physical education and mathematics as well. I wanted to do something that was more fun than physics, and to create additional options for the time after university. My own school days were still too close and graduation too far away for me to make up my mind about what I would do in the future.
I gradually warmed to the idea of becoming a school teacher. But I was pretty sure that it would not be physical education. I was attracted by the idea that teachers did not have to work a lot. For quite a while, my main goal in life was to have as much spare time as possible. Working non-stop, as I had been when I grew up on

the farm, was something I wanted to avoid under all circumstances. I did not receive any money from my parents, and I also did not get the standard scholarship from the German government (BAföG). From the very beginning I was financially on my own. One source of income was the little computer shop that I had launched as a student. But I did not need much money because I was very frugal. The greatest expense was my car. It cost me about 200 Deutschmarks per month back then. The rent for my first room was 180 Deutschmarks a month. Just as today, living quarters for students in Mainz were difficult to find and expensive. During my first semester, I lived in an eight square meter (86 sq ft) room, with the toilet in the hall. The landlady often came into my room unannounced. She had her own key. Sometimes she suddenly stood at the foot of my bed in the morning.

Over the years, I slowly moved up: first to ten square meters, then twelve, and finally to eighteen. I lived in a sort of private dorm in Bretzenheim, a suburb of Mainz. The kitchen and toilet were next to the courtyard on the ground floor, while the shower and the dorm's single phone were on the first floor. The telephone situation was a real nuisance—several women used to be on the phone for two or three hours at a time. I lived at the place for about three years, until my graduation in physics.

Looking back, it was a really nice time. I met people I still know today, such as a student of English and French who visits me with her pupils once a year at juwi, my company. Or Axel who was to become a vocational school teacher. He was sort of a house father: altogether, he had spent eight years in the Bretzenheim dorm, changing fields of study several times. He had a lot to tell the younger students. Later he played an important role in my life. The day before I was going to hand in my diploma thesis, Axel came to me with awful news. His girlfriend had left him. But not just like that. She had actually kicked him out—out of the house which they had built over several years. And as if that was not enough, her new boyfriend was to move in the next day. We went to a pub where we drank perhaps seven or eight glasses of beer each plus about as many shots of schnapps. I could not let him drown his sorrow all by himself. As we left the place, I reviewed, drunk as I was, everything we had discussed and also what I would tell my professor the next morning. I thus felt good and fit when I woke up some hours later, and the professor was satisfied. Poor Axel was clearly not in such a good mood for some time.

Start as an entrepreneur

My student years were marked by indecision. For a long time I did not know what I wanted to do and tried out many things. I know today that it was all about finding a purpose in life. Perhaps more importantly, I had to earn a living when I was a student, something many German youngsters have to do during their university years. So I had various jobs in my spare time and learned a lot about work. The first one, at an electrician, was hard—hammering slits into walls and floors, drilling holes into concrete and pulling wires for nine Deutschmarks an hour. That was a lot of work for little money. The next job was considerably better: 13.50 Deutschmarks at Dyckerhoff, the large cement producer. One thing was forbidden there—to work too hard! When I started to sweep the yard one day, colleagues immediately complained:
"Hey man, that's not how it works."
"Why? I'm good at this. I practiced it for years on the farm!" "But things are different here. If you work like a maniac, you set a bad example. So slow it down!"
In the early nineties—when I was just over 20 years old—I founded my first company. Computers were the main growth industry at the time. You could, of course, buy computers in a store, but they would not be customized. So I assembled "new" computers according to the specifications of my clients. I increased their storage capacity, added special graphic cards and so on. I made good money. I also enjoyed it. Per year I sold ten to fifteen computers, enough to keep me going as a physics student. But the business also caused me some sleepless nights because I always wanted to deliver top quality and be on time. Even back then I had the ambition to achieve optimal results.
At some point, I decided to earn my doctorate in Mainz. First of all, a teaching and research assistant at the university would earn a modest salary. In my case it was a half-time job, paid according to level 13A on the German civil service remuneration scale and thus a position for professionals. The other reason was that I could continue my physical education studies and run my computer business in Mainz. In the mornings I worked on the experiments for the dissertation called "Electric measurements on two-dimensional glass-like adsorbate films". It was about solid-state physics. I did the research at temperatures from minus 200 to about minus 270 degrees Celsius. Very boring. After that, I went to my physical education classes,

28

then back again to the experiment, and then on to the next class. The problem was: I still did not really know what I wanted. I only knew what I did not want: to become a physicist. And I also did not want to spend my entire life working. I could have earned a lot of money if I had focused on my computer business—it was exactly the right time for it. But being an around-the-clock computer specialist and businessman was not my thing. On the other hand, I did not want to worry about money. My father had always struggled to have enough money, for big-item purchases, for his children, and for retirement. I did not want that and found the idea of becoming a relaxed gym and math teacher much more attractive.

Then came the 25th of March 1995. One week before the last practical physical education exam, I had a rupture of a cruciate ligament. After a long night of partying, I had played soccer on a muddy field when a 100-kilo guy crashed into me. It was not intentional, just inability. The inner ligament was also torn, and a bone was splintered. Instead of taking exams, I ended up in a hospital, followed by intensive rehabilitation. After two and a half months, I was back riding my bicycle and played tennis again but still had to wear a bandage.

Two days after my first tennis match, on a Saturday, I was cycling to university. Another cyclist rode directly toward me—and then into me. I was coming from the right, had the right of way and had even stopped to let him pass. It did not help. On the Monday after the accident, I had to visit the doctor again. He punctured the knee several times. Three weeks later the same procedure. But now the knee was really swollen, and the pain was unbearable. I tried cooling it at home with vanilla ice cream, but it did not help. The pain would not go away. Apparently bacteria had entered the knee during puncturing. So I needed another surgery and had to spend two weeks of July 1995 in the Mainz University hospital.

A lucky coincidence changes my life

And there, in my bed, I read an article in the Mainzer Allgemeine Zeitung about people who had built a wind turbine near Prüm in the Eifel region. Up to this moment, I had never taken an interest in wind power. With the exception of basic electrical and mechanical principles, wind power did not play a role in my physics courses. While I had actually learned about photoelectric effects, the basis for solar power, real-life applications had never been a topic.

I was immediately fascinated. According to the article one could generate enough electricity from one single wind mill to supply 200 households for one year. I had never been politically active, and had never joined an anti-nuclear demonstration, nor was I ever particularly committed to or against any cause. I was anything but a deeply involved environmentalist, and certainly not "green". I had been a catholic altar boy, brought up conservatively and thinking like a conservative. The first time I was allowed to vote I ticked off the CDU (Christian Democratic Union) box. Where I come from, environmentalists and Greens are called "green wackos". My parents said: "We don't want to sit in the cold."

I did not want that either. When the "green wackos" claimed that newspapers were full of lies, especially about environmental issues, I thought: why would they lie? Today I know they were right. Many journalists are fairly uncritical and just reprint firms' and lobbyists' press releases.

Back then coal and nuclear power were OK for me. I was not anti-nuke. To get rid of nuclear power stations was certainly not my motivation for building a wind turbine. I simply thought it made economic and ecological sense. It helped that in 1991 chancellor Helmut Kohl's CDU/FDP (conservative/liberal) government had passed a law "on the storage of electricity from renewable energies in the public grid". This was the starting shot for the Energiewende.

At the time I came across the little story in the local press, there were simply no wind turbines in our region. The longer I thought about the question why this was so the more I became determined to do something about it. If the people from Prüm could do it, I could do it. We must build such a wind turbine near us, and I would be the one to do it.

3

The decisive moment

Why I became an entrepreneur in the renewable energy industry

It was like love at first sight. You cannot explain why sparks fly immediately when some person enters a room. That is how it was with the wind turbine and me. I had tried out a lot of things. I did not want to be a farmer, I found physics boring and I hated being in the lab every day. I am sure I could have become wealthy in the computer or software industry, but that did not appeal to me either. Without anything attractive to do, my goal was therefore to have as much free time as possible. Today I am aware that this wish just showed that I did not like what I had been doing so far.

But then for the first time in my life, tied to my hospital bed, I had the feeling: I want this. I absolutely want this. And I also know where I will build the wind mill: on my parents' property. They had given up farming. There was enough space. And there was plenty of wind.

And so I told everyone who visited me in the hospital that I would build a wind mill.

Did they really understand what I was talking about?

No matter. I knew what I wanted.

Discussions with the father

As it almost always is: some lucky coincidence gets things rolling. A fellow student had a brother. His name was Matthias. He worked in the public administration of the state of Hessen, one of the 16 German "Länder". His office in Wiesbaden, just across the Rhine from Mainz, was responsible for issuing permits for the installation of wind and solar power. Matthias had visited me in the hospital because he needed a computer. I had built him one and in return he told me what I had to do in order to get investment subsidies. I would have to apply for a wind certificate.

Four days after I had left the hospital, I drove with my girlfriend to the Eifel region to have a look at the wind mill described in the newspaper report. It was the first wind turbine that I had seen from up close.

We visited one of the designers. He was a teacher and wore knitted socks. He offered freshly pressed apple juice and explained everything to us. My girlfriend fell asleep on the sofa because things had become too theoretical. But I was fascinated, even though I did not understand everything I was told.

Shortly after this Matthias came to my parents' farm to have a look at the land where I was planning to put up a wind wheel. He was experienced in these matters and confirmed that the location was good. Then we had dinner with my parents. My father asked him all sorts of questions regarding wind power. He wanted to know how everything worked. When Matthias had left, my father asked: "How much will the thing actually cost?"

I said: "About a million."

My father looked at me and said: "No way. You won't do that."

I answered: "I'll do it."

And he: "If you do that, then you don't have to come back home anymore."

I understood him. He had worked hard every day for forty years so that his sons could get a good education and also to save a few Deutschmarks for old age—a farmer's pension used to be more than modest. My father feared that he would be liable in the event that something went wrong, and his sons would then inherit his debt. For him, this was a horrible prospect.

I had often discussed with him how to improve the efficiency of the farm and had made many suggestions. I had lots of ideas. For example, I suggested buying a machine that removes stones from the field, or a better hacking machine for turnips. But he only said: "No, we don't need that. We have always done things this way."

This was the usual end of our discussions. "We have always done things this way". I did not agree, but I had accepted that a topic was settled if he was against it.

It was the first time that I did not accept his "no". I was determined to change his mind and get him to say "yes". My brother suggested that we build a small wind wheel for perhaps 10,000 or 20,000 Deutschmarks. But I had already familiarized myself with the technical issues and knew that a small wind mill, ten meters high and inland, would not make economic sense. This is still true today. Small mills make financial sense in very few locations only, such as coastal areas where the wind is strong. As a physicist, I understood the relationship between the strength of the wind and electricity generation: increase the wind speed by a factor of 2 and you get eight times more electricity. In Wörrstadt, where my company has its headquarters today, the average wind speed at about 150 meters is twice the speed at 10 meters. No question: it would have to be a large wind mill.

Headwinds from the local utility

Finally, I found a way to convince my father. I would need other people to share the cost of the wind mill. I asked friends and acquaintances whether they could contribute. In two weeks, I had found eight investors, including my brother and my cousin's husband. I then went to my father and said: "Look, father, here are eight other crazy people. We will split the million by nine." I also took several of them to my parents' house. We explained to him that the risks were not so high after all—the potential liabilities of the partners would not exceed their shares in the venture.

It was important to me to convince my father that the project made financial sense and that the risks were limited. At some point, he gave in.

As I had learned from the teacher who had constructed a wind mill in the Eifel mountains I would need a connection to the grid. At a hearing at the state parliament in Mainz I had also met someone who was in charge of renewable energy at the Pfalzwerke, our regional electricity provider.

He was very friendly and seemed to support my project: "No problem, Mr. Willenbacher, I can help you to connect to the grid. Give me the address of the place where you want to construct the wind mill." And that's what I did.

He then drove to my parents and told them: "It's great what your son wants to do here. But he must be prepared for a rough ride—there are many obstacles." He tried to scare them. He almost succeeded. Not much, and my parents might have changed their mind again.

Obviously, the man from the utility had the task to advise people not to build wind mills. In 1995, German electricity markets had not yet been liberalized. Electricity companies were regional monopolists.

It would undermine their price setting ability if everyone started to produce and sell energy, including to business. Utilities were aware of the danger and fought anyone who might become a competitor. Decentralized and alternative electricity production was clearly such a danger. Advertisements from the established utilities claimed again and again that even in the long run renewables could not provide more than 5 per cent to the national electricity supply. In the 1993 ad on this page, the association of electricity providers actually asserts that sun, water and wind could at most cover 4 per cent of the demand for electricity!

The Pfalzwerke representative had used exactly those arguments in his talks with my parents. It took me some effort to convince them that I was on the right track after all. It was a close call.

In early 1996 I went to the state agency that had the final say about the construction of wind mills. There, the response was "What are you up to? It is difficult to approve something like this."

An approval was needed to get a grant from the Land. I had to get it fast because there was only money for 15 applicants, and it was distributed on a first come-first serve basis. Since 1994, as the successor of Rudolf Scharping, Kurt Beck had been the head of a social-liberal coalition government in Mainz, the capital of Rhein-land-Pfalz. This is how they had begun to support wind energy. In order to speed up things, I did the errands around the offices of the state bureaucracy myself. I got the construction permit after only five weeks. To this day, no one at juwi has been faster in this respect. One week later, I also received the grant: 216,000 Deutschmarks, or about 20 per cent of the total investment. With the grant, the construction approvals, the lease agreement and the wind experts' reports in hand, we went to my father's bank. The banker bombarded me with questions—how many wind expert opinions did I have, whether I actually had a construction approval, what my lease agreement for the land looked like, and what would be the profita-bility over the coming 20 years? I was well prepared and able to answer everything to his satisfaction. Most people who were plan-ning to construct wind mills back then were less successful. Many started to negotiate with their banks before they had taken care of all the technical, administrative and financial details. When they heard what the bankers were asking for, they were often discour-aged. I was somehow aware that it didn't make much sense to talk to the bank before I had all necessary documents and feasibility studies. The next day, a bank approved the 600,000 Deutschmark loan! So three fifths of the investment came from the bank, one fifth was a grant from our state government, and one fifth came from the nine of us.

Meeting with Fred from Kibo

At this point, Fred Jung enters the picture. He was an agricultural economist from Kirchheimbolanden, where I had gone to school. The name of the town is too long, so we abbreviated it to Kibo. What I did not know back then: there was a whole bunch of people in our county, the "Donnersbergkreis" (thunder mountain!), who were thinking about wind mills. Fred was one of them. My first wind test series with the air speed meter from Matthias was incomplete. His device was only a prototype. The risk to invest on the basis of wrong numbers was too high for me—after all, I was about to spend one million Deutschmarks. Everything had to be right.
Therefore, I went to the Meteorological institute in Mainz to see what could be done. I met a doctoral student there by the name of Roland who wrote a thesis about a three-dimensional simulation model for determining wind speeds. Doing some calculations for me

was a nice empirical addition to his dissertation—and I got another wind expertise. But even that was not enough to assure the reliability of the data. Therefore, my fellow investors and I did some measurements of our own. My father chopped down a tree. We dragged it out of the forest and put it up again in the field. With the help of a tractor, I attached measurement devices to the tree, eight meters above ground. That was quite dangerous: it was the end of January and it was snowing heavily. But it had to be done no matter what because I urgently needed the data.

At the agency which had given me the construction permit I had heard of about twenty other people who were also planning to install wind mills. One of them was Fred. He was probably conducting wind measurements on his parents' farm, I thought. We were both farmers' sons and had begun, independently from one another, to pursue the same idea.

I kept calling this guy called Fred and finally found him in his student dorm in Stuttgart-Hohenheim. We agreed to meet at his family's farm. When I arrived there, many people were sitting in the kitchen. They were rehearsing wedding songs for a friend of Fred's. Together they had prepared "Grumbeersupp", the region's popular potato soup. Fred said: "Come eat with us."

I thought it was very nice that I was accepted by the group right away. And it was also nice that Fred let me see his measurement data. The first meeting with him was great.

After eating, we drove to the field where he wanted to place his wind mill. His data covered one year while mine were just for four weeks. But my results for the period for which we both had data were considerably better than his. My average wind speed was about 4.5 meters per second. His average for the whole year was around four meters per second, a very good number for wind ten meters above ground. However, he was still at an early stage because he was not able to connect to the grid. That is different today. At the time of this writing (2014), an electric power transformation station stands on the site that Fred had chosen back then. It is used to feed electricity into the giant overhead power lines of the German grid. In 2013, ten 3-megawatt wind mills were built on the property.

A few people with whom I worked had a close look at wind turbines produced by firms such as Tacke, Micon, Vestas and Enercon. The first two companies no longer exist. They were bought up by competitors. We decided that Enercon was best for us. The north German wind turbine manufacturer had two important advantages in the generator class of up to 0.5 megawatts: a gearless generator and the highest tower, 65 meters. As I said, winds are stronger higher up. Moreover, our site was hilly and surrounded by forests. In such an environment, far away from the coast, tall towers are absolutely necessary for the success of the decentralized Energiewende. Today, new towers at inland locations are around 140 meters high (460 feet).

Bernhard, the salesman from Enercon responsible for southwest Germany, came to see me personally in my student apartment in Mainz and asked: "Do you have financing?"

I said: "Yes, sure."

That was it. I did not have to prove anything.

I said: "I have one request. Could you do most of the work within the next four weeks? I have time now because the semester has not yet begun."

"No problem. We'll start next week."

I had never bought anything big, never spent more than 5,000 Deutschmarks. The Enercon contract was for 940,000 Deutschmarks. My hands shook when I looked at it. I covered the last three digits so that only the number 940 was showing—I could sign that. Together with the outlays for the grid connection, the expert wind reports, for various approvals and for this and that, we had reached more than one million Deutschmarks.

That was a bit more than the initial goal of 100,000 Deutschmarks for each of the nine partners. We had promised to each other at the beginning of the project that we would do everything together; everyone would stay equal. But in the end, it did not work. Each of us was motivated differently; contributions were also different. The coordination processes were quite time consuming. Just to agree on the name of the company took us five weeks, three or four meetings and endless rounds of voting—without results. In the end, the company's name was „Schwinge", shorthand for Schneeberger Windkraftanlagen Gesellschaft mbH.

In spite of these delays, it only took a little over nine months to get from the initial idea in the hospital to the completion of the wind mill. That was, above all, because I was so ridiculously stubborn. I wanted the wind mill more than anything else in the world. At the end of July 1995, I had read the article in the Mainz daily, and in May 1996 I had got my wind mill. Even though the collaboration with the eight others—Fred Jung was not a member of that group—was not always easy, I am very grateful to each and every one of them. My dream could only be realized with their help. Incidentally, the tower was not built on my father's ground but on my uncle's nearby: his was the better location.

"My first wind mill"

Woodstock at Schneebergerhof

For seven years, the generator of the wind mill produced, on average, 30 per cent more electricity than we had expected. After that, the station was repowered, with a larger generator, a higher tower (its axis was at 100 meters) and rotors with a diameter of 70 rather than 40 meters. Since then, its annual electricity output has been four times larger.

In 2010 we also repowered an older generator at Schneebergerhof with an E 126 model from Enercon which produces 7.5 megawatts or 18 times more than our first wind mill. That shows the incredibly fast progress in wind technology. In total, six wind mills and an open-area photovoltaic facility are presently on the property. They generate enough electricity to supply a city of 40,000 residents.

The official inauguration of our first wind mill was on July 13, 1996. That day was later called "Woodstock at Schneebergerhof" and has become a key date in the history of the village. I climbed to the top of the tower and looked down from high up—what I saw had never before happened anywhere in the region: all roads and lanes were full of cars, and the fields were full of people. 3,500 had come for the occasion. They had travelled from the Taunus north of Frankfurt, from Pirmasens at the southern border of our Land, and even from Baden-Württemberg, more than 100 kilometers to the south-east. Some may have come for the beer and the music, but most just wanted to see their first wind mill and to learn about the new technology: how can electricity profitably be generated from wind?

It was a day of great euphoria. The term "Energiewende" was not yet popular, but the search for alternative sources of energy had begun. It was something like a wind mill fest: hey, here is a genuine alternative. And: if even students can do it, the technology must have a lot of potential.

It was a huge party which lasted well into the night. My birthday actually began at midnight.

We opened the last 50-liter keg of beer at four in the morning, determined to empty the entire thing. But it was too much. I took the keg home and a few days later we continued to celebrate and drank the rest.

One of my friends said he had brought me a birthday present, "the coolest computer game in the world". He was going to load it onto my computer. He did, but the next day my hard drive was completely useless—including my doctoral dissertation. Luckily, I had made a back-up disc, just in case, which I kept in my rucksack. According to Murphy's Law, it was exactly in a spot where a bottle of typewriter correction fluid had spilled its content—directly onto the disc. Nothing could be done about it. I later saved portions of the thesis on a computer at the university, but 80 per cent of the thesis was gone.

The final decision

I had already orally defended my dissertation. Normally, you can hand it in in written form up to half a year later. I worked on the text for several months to restore what had been lost. But in the meantime, Fred Jung and I had already founded juwi. At the end of 1996, we received the approval for another wind mill. And a few months later, we got permits for four more. At that point I was seriously asking myself: should I really finish my doctorate now and become a physical education instructor? Or should I do what obviously kept me busy and totally satisfied? Basically, the answer was clear.

In April 1997, my professor came to me and said: "Mr. Willenbacher, things cannot continue this way. You have to try harder, otherwise you won't get your doctorate."
I answered: "You are completely right, I should try harder, but I don't want to do it anymore. I quit."
He was incredulous because he had just wanted to wake me up. But I had thought about it long enough. The decisive moment had come. It was a liberating. I was now 27 and I would neither become a teacher nor a civil servant. Nor was I looking for a secure position as an employee in industry, like my brother who was at BASF at the time. I would not finish my doctorate thesis. I would be an entrepreneur and promote renewable energies—now. I was committed to the cause one hundred per cent.
The company had already been set up. Together, Fred and I had built four wind turbines at the time—on the side. We had made plans to meet in my student apartment directly the day after the installation of the first wind turbine. It was May 16, 1996, Ascension Day, a public holiday in Germany.
We talked to each other, and after a while I said to him: "We could build a wind turbine together. But I don't want to discuss the name for weeks."
I definitely did not want that after my previous experience of agreeing on the "Schwinge" name.
But Fred Jung had already stretched out his hand and said: "Ju".
I looked at him and said: "Wi".
That was the beginning of our company, juwi. And that is the nature of our collaboration to this day. We often say spontaneously: This is how we'll do it now.
And then we do it.

And this is how we do it even today. Fred (on the left) and I at the 10th "juwilee"

4

The Energiewende is a bottom-up project

From protest movement to decentralized energy production

I still remember exactly the moment when we had built the first juwi wind mill near Kirchheimbolanden. Fred and I stood underneath the tower and looked across the wide and empty high plain.
"Look at this, Fred", I said, "as far as you can see—not a single village. We will build a large wind park there."
Fred was less excited: "Matthias, let's wait a few years before we continue in this area."
We had just learned the hard way what it means when ordinary citizens are not involved early on in the process of putting up wind mills in their neighborhood.
A typical beginner's mistake: a wind mill was planned somewhere between the villages of Ilbesheim and Stetten. It would stand on land belonging to Stetten. The people from that village were therefore asked whether they agreed to its construction—they did. But the citizens of Ilbesheim were not asked. They did not know anything about the project, would not benefit from it and were anything but amused.
Back then, I was 27, Fred Jung was 26. In the town hall meeting in Ilbesheim people were outraged and we realized that we were still inexperienced youngsters.
They shouted "do you have a written permit?"
I said "sure" and held it up.
That infuriated them even more: the wind mill would be two kilometers from the center of Stetten, but only 500 meters from Ilbesheim—and therefore more or less in their front yard.
The storm of protest was fully justified. People felt passed over and were angry.
Afterwards, some of them actually approached us and asked how they could invest in such projects. Still, it was the perfect example

of a messed-up decision process. I was not yet aware of how important it is to involve everyone who has a stake in a project. To this day you get a classic conflict when wind towers are built on town limits if the benefits only go to one community while the negative externalities are dumped on the other. It is important that both sides gain.

Another insight: there is never just one action group. There are many, as well as strategic alliances where people with different goals work together. The impetus usually comes from people who hate to have wind mills near their house. They are concerned about their health or expect that the value of their house might go down.

If someone does not want to live near a wind turbine, I respect that. And if someone feels that these tall towers spoil the beauty of the land, I cannot convince them otherwise. But this is not my view: I am impressed by the technology and feel that most wind mills are very beautiful. I have to admit, there are places where you don't want to have them. On the other hand, they make a lot of sense, in a lot of ways—and that is why I will always be an advocate of wind energy.

The strategy of the big energy utilities

What are the arguments of those who oppose wind mills? It is worth taking a closer look. The views of conservationists are very important to me. We want to align their interests with those of the environmentalists rather than playing one off against the other. I have learned, though, that the conservation of nature is often used as an excuse to block the Energiewende.

In my early years, the main argument was that wind mills were useless. It was the strategy of the electricity utilities: they obviously wanted to protect their business models and profits against new competitors. It was clear to them that renewables were a serious challenge. Once electricity production from these sources made business sense, lots of new players would enter the market and transform it fundamentally, at the expense of the oligopolists. As it was, the employees of established utilities provided the anti-wind mill initiatives with arguments. Sometimes it was difficult to differentiate between the interests of the action groups and those of the utilities fighting for their business interests. For a long time, RWE, E.on, Vattenfall and EnBW took it as granted that it was their god-given role to control the energy policies of the country.

Since its founding in 1995, the German Association for Landscape Preservation (BLS) has campaigned against the "threats of wind power stations". The BLS has always rejected the accusation of environmentalists and conservationists that it was actually a lobby for the established energy providers. But its leading representatives' skeptical views about wind power were frequently voiced in the SPIEGEL, the influential German weekly magazine. The high point of the war against wind power was an article in the spring of 2003 entitled "The Big Flop". After its publication, two critical journalists who had specialized on Energiewende issues protested by handing in their resignations from the magazine.

In those years, the initial euphoria about wind energy had turned into skepticism. Reasons were the inadequate involvement of affected citizens, local resistance and well-organized counterstrikes by the energy establishment. By 1998, when juwi's wind mill business began to take off, the opponents had already lined up their forces. The more wind mills we put up, the stronger the opposition.

In the summer of 1999 there were local government elections in my home state of Rheinland-Pfalz. Mayors who had welcomed us before all of a sudden withdrew their support. They were scared by the increasing opposition against wind power. Their earlier commitment was denounced as destroying landscape and nature, and as undemocratic. I learned the hard way that protest movements are very effective before elections. The main goal of politicians is to get elected or re-elected. It's as easy as that.

Around this time, the planning board "Westpfalz" had presented a wind power map of the region. To us, it suggested that one could put up wind turbines in the places identified as favorable locations. So we leased several of these. It turned out, however, that the concept had neither been coordinated with the local communities nor with the organizations of the conservationists.

Showdown in Schallodenbach

One of these locations was Schallodenbach, in the county of Kaiserslautern. On a range of hills we had planned to install twenty wind mills; a competitor had planned another ten. So there were to be 30 wind mill towers in a relatively small area. To make matters worse, we intended to construct additional wheels on a near-by property— the planning authority had confirmed that the land was eligible for such a project.

The show-down took place in the fall of 1999, at a townhall meeting in Schallodenbach. This is a village where many people had moved from the city to live in an unspoiled natural environment. Banners and posters against wind power were all over the place. At the local elections not long before the meeting, the supporters of wind power had been heavily defeated. As a result, the district administrator ("Landrat") was forced to swear off all wind mills; the newly elected mayor promised: "only over my dead body!" Politicians, new residents, nature lovers and environmentalists—they all wanted to safeguard their "Heimat", their homeland.

Against us!

I can still remember one poster in the hall in front of me: "Mommy, save my town!"

In the following hour I was confronted with all the arguments that have been used to stop wind power right from the beginning: the tower and the rotor blades would cast shadows, birds would be killed, real estate prices would collapse, and the assertion that electricity from wind mills could never be more than a "drop in the ocean"—the rising demand for electricity could only be met by the traditional sources of energy. My favorite came up as well: "What if the wind doesn't blow? Don't we then sit in the dark? It's better to leave things as they are. Wind mills are useless."

That was also the time when large energy producers ran series of ads claiming that the electricity grid could not absorb more than an additional five per cent from renewables. The Pfalzwerke utility again and again blocked wind mill connections to the grid, arguing that it could not handle them. At Schneebergerhof, for instance, we wanted to construct a new wind mill with a 1.5 megawatt generator; the old one, built in 1997, had a capacity of 500 kilowatts. It would be the first on-shore generator with so much power. The Pfalzwerke initially prohibited the feed-in of the full electricity output in the hope that I would then give up on the project. I didn't. After the wind mill had been connected to the grid, we conducted measurements of the voltage and the frequencies. The result was that the grid could easily accommodate the additional electricity, ie, the full output of the wind mill. The Pfalzwerke had to give in a few days later.

Two years after that, we had the same discussion. We wanted to put up two further wind mills at one location. It took an expert appraiser from northern Germany, letters from our lawyers and a lot of pressure to get the permits. While the grid had the same capacity as before, it was suddenly possible to feed in 4,500 kilowatts after all, nine times more than at the beginning when the 500 kilowatt mill had supposedly created huge problems. The fundamental issue was that Pfalzwerke, the regional electricity monopolist, wanted to prevent competition from renewables.

In the meantime, the utility is also in the business of wind mills, photovoltaic installations and bio gas. Board members had changed their minds. It helped that Pfalzwerke is not operating any major conventional power plant. But in the beginning its strategy was: as few wind mills as possible.

For them, the main points were that wind mills are not useful, harm the natural habitat and spoil the landscape. The strategy to shock people with such arguments worked quite well that evening in the Schallodenbach townhall.

The discussions get personal

It was a tough encounter. As I stepped down from the stage, relieved, I seem to have smiled a little. I remember very well the woman who approached me after the event. She was in her mid-forties and probably, in normal circumstances, a polite person. But now she looked at me full of animosity: "You won't be smiling for much longer. I'm actually tempted to punch you right in the face."

We had several such confrontations in those years. Often, the tires of my colleagues' cars were slashed, and in general our opponents played hardball.

There was a mayor in the Vogelsberg county in the state of Hesse who had advocated wind power from early on. When the question of wind power was raised in Flomborn, in the hills of the Rhinehesse region south of Mainz, we hired a bus and drove people to the Vogelsberg to show them how things could work out. That convinced many of them. Soon after, we were able to construct 13 wind mills in Flomborn. Then the village next door also wanted to have some. "We will have them here as well", said the mayor and set everything in motion for 15 wind mills. A storm of protests followed.

Trude, a winegrower, started a protest movement against wind power. She created a website called "Hügelland" (hill country) and published a leaflet for people in the six or seven villages around the planned wind park. Readers were kept up-to-date about the latest developments in the planning process. From our point of view, all reports had a negative touch.

The action group was quite professional. It networked with similar groups in other places, improved its know-how in this way and flooded government agencies with documents that were supposed to show that wind mills did not make sense—especially not at the planned sites. It put increasing pressure on the town and county administrations, the state government, its minister for the environment, the premier minister of the Land (state), and all media. But the mayor, the village and the "Verbandsgemeinde" (association of several villages) continued to support us.

Then we got anonymous hate mail, including my parents. "If your son does not stop it, something terrible will happen." The letter was not signed, but the address was handwritten.

"Very good", I thought. That is a lead.

At a public hearing, I handed out an attendance list for people to sign—I wanted to identify the handwriting.

But the winemaker Trude had become suspicious, and when I was about to leave the room with the list she yelled "Stop Willenbacher!" A heavily built man grabbed me just outside and threw me against the wall. "Give me the list!" I didn't—and called for help.

The mayor came running and took the list.

In the internet you can still read how my "scandalous behavior", which bordered on "fraudulent cheating", had "shocked" people at the meeting.

This reads like a farce from a wild past. I think it gives a good impression of how things were during this phase of the Energiewende.

Instrumentalization of the man in the street

The main tool of wind power opponents back then was a book published in 1997 by Otfried Wolfrum, a professor at the Technical University in Darmstadt: "Wind power: an alternative that isn't" ("Windkraft: Eine Alternative, die keine ist"). The book had been published, of all things, by Zweitausendeins, which has the reputation of being green and left. Wolfrum was a landscape conservationist and gave the book the subtitle "the collected disinformation about wind energy".

"Windy Protest" ("Windiger Protest") was another influential book. Edited by the longtime TV journalist Franz Alt together with Jürgen Claus and the SPD politician and environmentalist Hermann Scheer, it was released in 1998. The authors analyze the motives of wind power opponents.

Wolfrum described wind power as an over-subsidized form of energy which requires lots of space but would never contribute significantly to overall electricity production. He also had his doubts about the potential for new jobs in this sector. Additionally, wind power was too expensive for exports. And it would eliminate incentives to improve energy efficiency.

All of this is refuted in "Windy Protest", the pro-Energiewende book. Scheer had identified two different camps of opponents; these had formed a "negative coalition". On the one side were the landscape and nature conservationists for whom the "aesthetic contamination of the landscape" and the preservation of nature are more important issues than pollution from fossil fuel emissions or the risks of radioactivity. Then there were the established producers of electricity from uranium and fossil-fuels which earn a lot of money but see their profits threatened by independent and decentralized wind energy operators. They tried to discourage the new market participants by making it difficult for them to access the grid. Given their considerable political influence they were able to slow or prevent progress; the complicated legal environment worked in their favor. All arguments they could think of were employed to confuse consumers and turn them into opponents of wind power. Both the angst of common people and the concerns of environmentalists were instrumentalized.

In Schallodenbach, the defenders of the status quo looked around long and hard until they found an endangered bird of prey, Montagu's harrier, which was supposedly breeding near the site of the future towers. The argument could not be held up court, and in the end the wind mills could actually be constructed.

It was and is not easy to fight against the same prejudices and arguments again and again. Even today, many people are convinced that the entire project is useless—you have to be crazy to believe renewable energies could seriously replace nuclear and fossil power. They also claim that revenues from alternative energy production cannot really make a difference for the budgets of local governments—on the other hand, the subsidies would fill the pockets of "green" wheeler-dealers. Not to forget the recurring claim that wind is not a reliable source of energy; it simply does not blow all the time.

It is true that wind power cannot provide a steady flow of electricity. Other sources are needed as well. But that does not at all mean we should not use as much wind power as possible. To fill the gap, the power of the sun should be added to the mix.

Ironically, it was my former German teacher, Roland, who convinced me that sun power was an indispensable addition to our wind mill projects.

This teacher was, to be honest, not exactly very popular at our school. He often told me "Matthias, sit straight. Didn't your parents teach you to sit up straight?"

He was an active conservationist who regarded the protection of the local bird population as his mission in life. Wind towers were therefore a horror for him. One day, I met him by chance at a town hall meeting. He was the leader of the local wind power critics who tried to prevent the destruction of the landscape and to preserve nature—regardless of the global effects on climate. Highways, landfills, wind mills: for him, they were all the same.

"People like you—physicists, engineers—are not at all able to understand the natural environment" he argued. "Only philologists understand what it's all about."

Only people like him.

On the other hand, a former history teacher of mine was excited by the looks of wind mills. His priority was the clean production of energy. For him, wind mills were displacing the old industrial landscape. They were aesthetically appealing and created a new kind of environment—with a global ecological and social dimension. I guess that about ten per cent of people find wind mills aesthetically pleasing while another ten per cent find them ugly and will always reject them for this reason—regardless of how useful they are. The remaining 80 per cent are ambivalent. Their attitude is: if it makes economic and environmental sense, we are in favor.

Great vistas are not an argument against wind power

Renewable energies should not come at the expense of nature. Here I agree with the conservationists. But the beauty of the land and nice vistas are not the most important arguments for me. If one is truly convinced of renewable energies, environmentalists will always be able to accommodate the interests of the conservationists. It is possible; we have enough open spaces in Germany.

I still remember how my brother told me to put up my first wind mill in a place where my father could not see it—in the early years, he was against it. I answered that this would not be an option for me. "I don't want to hide what I am doing. My aim is to convince the folks in my neighborhood, the people I know".

My alternative energy project is in their interest, not against it. It is not asking too much to make compromises. Man has always changed the landscape, especially in central Europe. It was worth it, and still is.

What I do not like is the not-in-my-backyard attitude. Many people try to combine a passionate rejection of wind mills with accepting them for theoretical and fundamental reasons: "I agree, wind mills and renewable energy are extremely important, but please not next to my house. I will vehemently fight against such projects in this location."

If you agree that electricity production from renewables is important, you should be prepared to compromise. Ask what would be the best locations for the wind mills rather than simply say you are against them nearby. Incidentally, I find the wind mills at Schneeberger Hof visually attractive.

It is important to fight back

Even though the big energy producers continue to instrumentalize local and national protest movements against wind mills in order to obstruct or slow down the Energiewende and to protect their profits from "dirty" electricity, I find civil protest and engagement extremely important. People must be able to fight for their interests, especially if they are confronted with large and destructive projects. In the case of the planned wide corridors for power lines from the north to the south of Germany, I find it absolutely necessary to fight back. The corridors serve the interests of the established electricity producers. But they are not needed. The Energiewende is about a world where electricity is generated in a decentralized way.

It is important to realize that protest movements, be they justified or not, cannot stop the Energiewende. Because of its decentralized nature, it has considerable momentum by now. There are some areas where protests have succeeded to prevent wind mills, for instance in the Pfälzer Wald, a very large forest area and a nature preserve in the south of our Land, north of the Alsace region in France. But there are plenty of other locations where wind mills are widely accepted. For every 20 local communities which are against there are 200 that regard the Energiewende as an opportunity. Most importantly, they know that electricity no longer simply comes from a socket in the wall. In addition, they see electricity from renewables as a source of additional revenue and a compensation for the weakness of their traditional sources of income. It gives them the means to stimulate the local economy and create something sustainable for future generations. It is possible these days to use the local electricity corridors for internet lines as well, thus killing two birds with one stone.

As to the concern that tourism will suffer from wind mills and the like, there is in the meantime a countermovement: renewable energy installations as tourist destinations. This includes, for example, Freiburg's eco district, Vauban, and the solar park nearby; the Morbach energy park; the solar ships on Lake Constance; or wind mill towers with observation platforms, as in Holtriem. Our own Schneebergerhof has also become such a destination for tourists. These days, about 9,000 people a year are visiting our headquarters in Wörrstadt, including school classes and country ladies' clubs.

Citizens are the drivers of the Energiewende

Protest movements which aimed to prevent wind power have inadvertently stabilized the oligopoly of the large utilities. The new action groups, on the other hand, play a very positive role. Their focus is on decentralized and clean energy production and thus automatically on the redistribution of electricity revenues from the big players to local stake holders.

These stake holders are now the drivers of the Energiewende.

They are increasingly generating electricity themselves—for example by installing photovoltaic panels on their roofs or storage facilities in their basements. In this way, they do no longer depend on the oligopolistic electricity suppliers or on burning fossil fuels. They also contribute to the Energiewende by participating in the political decision making process and by resisting the obstruction strategies of the oligopolists and their allies. One example of this is the campaign "The Energiewende—energy production by you and me". Participants are the "100 prozent erneuerbar stiftung" (100 per cent renewables foundation), the BUND, BürgerEnergie Berlin eG, Energiewende Jetzt (now), the GLS Bank Foundation and the Haleakala Foundation. They fight for what most people really want: the expansion of the renewables sector and a genuine Energiewende.

"Approval rates for renewable energy sites in one's neighborhood—and whether approval rates increase as a function of one's familiarity with renewables"

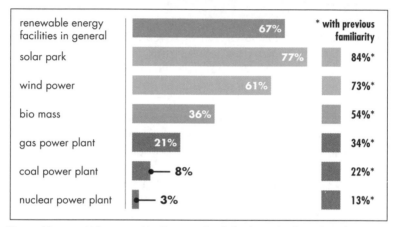

		* with previous familiarity
renewable energy facilities in general	67%	
solar park	77%	84%*
wind power	61%	73%*
bio mass	36%	54%*
gas power plant	21%	34%*
coal power plant	8%	22%*
nuclear power plant	3%	13%*

"Renewables are widely accepted by Germans. People familiar with solar and wind power are very positive about electricity production from renewables in their neighborhood." Source: www.unendlich-viel-energie.de/de/detailansicht/browse/1/article/226/

At the end of 2012, a survey by TNS Infratest showed that 77 per cent of Germans had a positive attitude toward solar sites and 61 per cent toward wind mills in their neighborhood. Coal-burning power plants only have an eight per cent approval rate, nuclear power plants just nine per cent. Opposition against renewable energy is strongest where people have little influence on the planning process and do not profit financially because the money for the projects comes from investment funds. Wind parks run by local people usually enjoy a high level of acceptance.

Booming energy cooperatives

Energy cooperatives are booming in Germany. Between 2007 and 2013, their number grew by a factor of almost nine, to 888. Together, they had more than 150,000 members. Growth has been explosive. The reason for the boom is the wish and willingness of people to participate: they want to help, but they also want to have a say in the decision process. And they want to benefit financially.

As members of energy cooperatives they can get involved, invest money and expect an income flow right from the beginning. Potential personal liabilities are capped by the amount of money invested. Most energy cooperatives have been launched in states with plenty of open spaces: Bavaria, Baden-Württemberg and Lower Saxony. In Baden-Württemberg, the boom was triggered by technological advances in energy production from renewables and the change of government from CDU/FDP (conservative/liberal) to Greens/SPD (Social Democrats). According to the state's Ministry of the Environment, the number of energy cooperatives has risen dramatically, from ten in 2008 to something like 150 today. "Cooperatives are an important element in the development of renewable energies—the Energiewende is a grass roots project", as Baden-Württemberg's Minister for the Environment, Franz Untersteller, likes to say. The 2012 EEG-Novelle (an amendment to the Renewable Energy Act, the EEG) has led to a massive decline in solar park projects, which were the favorites of the energy cooperatives until recently. Guaranteed feed-in tariffs have been significantly reduced. According to the revised EEG, large solar parks are no longer subsidized. Energy cooperatives have therefore begun to focus on wind parks.

An example of an energy cooperative is the "BürgerEnergie Tauberfranken" which runs two solar parks and can hardly meet demand. Additional sun and wind energy parks are in the planning phase. The executives and the members of the supervisory board are all volunteers which is why the cooperative neither builds new facilities nor develops the projects—it hires experienced service providers such as juwi to build the cooperative solar park Tauberfranken. It is important to me personally to support the cooperatives. Only the citizens themselves can generate the necessary enthusiasm and support in their communities. When the issue is to provide a structure that channels the revenue from the renewables projects to local investors, we can help with our know-how. We have been in the business for 18 years.

The people who are active in energy cooperatives are often strongly influenced by the green movement of the last three decades. They know their enemies. Joachim Thees, for example, of the board of BürgerEnergie Tauberfranken says his enthusiasm for clean and decentralized energy comes from Grafenrheinfeld, a nuclear power plant close to Schweinfurt, his hometown in northern Bavaria (in March 2014, E.on has announced that it will switch off Grafenrheinfeld in May 2015).

The fundamental difference to the political movements of the past is the motivation: it is no longer about preventing the worst. The members of the energy cooperatives want to shape the future, environmentally and economically. The BürgerEnergie Tauberfranken consists of young families and retired people who invest for their grandchildren. At 500 euros, the minimum share is set so low that almost everyone can participate. In addition, the maximum amount is limited so that large investors cannot become too influential. In this way, the democratic element of the Energiewende is protected. The cooperatives are important for the social dynamics and a decentralized structure that is independent of the large electricity providers.

Increasing number of energy cooperatives in Germany

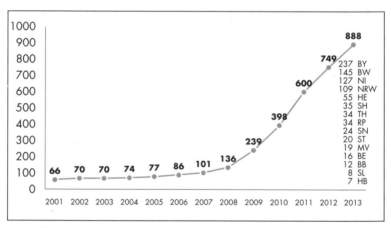

Source: Klaus Novy Institute; 1/2014
In the past six years, the number of energy cooperatives has increased by a factor of almost nine; the right-hand column stands for the number of cooperatives in 15 of the 16 German states.

The civil society

A further vehicle for the advancement of the Energiewende is a legal structure called "GmbH and Co. KG". It is a private limited partnership where members are not "Genossen" (associates) but shareholders.
Erich Wust is director of "Wust–Wind & Sonne". He oversees numerous wind energy sites in Bavaria, owned by GmbH and Co. KGs—and thus mostly by locals. "The role of local people is very important. It

is also important that they have the impression that each and every one of them is a small but significant part of the larger project called Energiewende", he says. The Bavarian wind parks, located in the supposedly low wind speed areas of southern Germany, use state-of-the-art technology. Even in months with less wind than expected, the electricity output remains on target so far. With hubs 140 meters above ground and rotor diameters of more than 100 meters, it is possible to achieve good results. Wust–Wind & Sonne takes care of business and technical issues as well as civic participation; it also identifies the best project developer. We at juwi Group work closely with those small Bavarian energy producers and have already projected facilities for them. Wust is a committed champion of a grassroots approach to developing the future energy system.

Another exciting example is the "BürgerEnergie Berlin Cooperative" which wants to buy the electricity grid from the city state Berlin when the concession of Sweden's Vattenfall, the current operator, expires in 2014. The idea is that those who use the grid and pay for it via their electricity bills should be able to make the relevant decisions and get a share in the profits. Responsibility would thus rest with people who are committed to the Energiewende rather than with a large utility which prefers fossil and nuclear inputs—Vattenfall's existing plants still generate lots of profits!

The municipal utilities are important for the success of the Energiewende. They can produce and deliver clean energy—electricity and heat—via stakes in renewable energy producers or by building wind and solar parks. In this way, they create value instead of spending money on energy imports.

A good example for modern local energy policies is Stadtwerke Schwäbisch Hall. Managing Director Johannes van Bergen has transformed it into a municipal energy company which benefits the region and promotes the Energiewende. According to the Stuttgarter Zeitung and other media, Schwäbisch Hall is therefore a "pioneer of the Energiewende".

Another positive example is the local utility in Mainz; it is 100 per cent owned by the city. However, the change of heart came only in response to significant pressure from the city's population. At a time when coal-powered plants were still acceptable, the cities of Mainz and Wiesbaden, just across from each other on the Rhine, had joined forces to build such a power plant on the Ingelheimer Aue, an island in the river. The citizens, however, were able prevent it—on the one hand through local initiatives, on the other hand because the 2009 local elections in Mainz had become a vote on the coal project which was backed by a grand coalition of CDU (conservatives), SPD (Social Democrats) and FDP (liberals). The result: the Greens who had campaigned against the project won no less than 21.9 per cent of the vote, after 14.3 per cent five years before, while the pro-coal SPD shrank from 28.8 to 23.8 per cent. Under pressure from its own constituency, the CDU was forced to switch sides in the debate about the new power plant. In the end, even the SPD found reasons why it was not such a good idea. By the end of 2009, the new "traffic light" coalition (red Social Democrats, yellow Liberals and green Greens) officially cancelled the project. Since then the Mainzer Stadtwerke, the local utility, has launched an "Energiewende for the future" campaign and is finally on the road to modernity.

But it only worked because people had said loud and clear that they did not want dirty coal power plants anymore. The problem is not just carbon dioxide and its effect on the climate, but also particulate matter, sulfur dioxide, nitrogen oxide, cadmium and mercury emissions. These imperil human health and cause huge external costs. As it is, most members of CDU, CSU and FDP, the "coal wing" of the SPD as well as a few Greens still believe that the Energiewende can be achieved by cooperating with the big boys, the oligopolistic utilities which have split up the country among themselves.

That is a fundamental mistake. The Energiewende will lead to a totally new system, away from a powerful few which collude to fix electricity prices toward millions of households who are committed to the democratization of energy. The priority of the large players is to maximize their profits. If they had been willing to make less than those almost 20 billion euros (before interest and tax) which they earned in 2012, customers' electricity bills would have been much lower. A genuine Energiewende based on decentralized electricity production, local utilities, energy cooperatives and energy parks needs the support of the general public.

People have often asked me why revenues from a wind mill were morally superior to dividends from corporate stocks. The management of RWE is only interested in return on investment while most people who participate in renewable energy projects have other motives as well. That is the difference.

Many people are fascinated by the Energiewende because they want to become independent of outside sources and like clean energy.

These are the drivers of the transition process. And that is why I know what I will do with my shares of juwi AG, should chancellor Merkel accept my "indecent" proposal and in fact implement the Energiewende by 2020: I will give my money to the cooperatives. There it is in good hands. These people fight for a decentralized Energiewende, for their participation in the project and for clean energy.

At the highpoint of the discussion at the townhall meeting in Schallodenbach, my former German teacher, Roland, had asked me, "and what do you do when the wind doesn't blow, Matthias?". It was the classic question.

To counter this argument with something new and powerful, I said "when the wind is not strong enough, we still have the sun. So we'll build solar parks." This is what we then did at juwi as well.

It took a trip to Africa to make me aware of the future role of solar energy.

5

The best development aid is a solar panel

How locally generated solar power promotes global justice

Almost two billion people have to live without electricity. They would not have access even if a new miracle energy source were to be found. For as long as electricity and the power grid are managed centrally, they will get no access. In certain rural areas of Africa there will never be power lines. For one thing, it is often difficult to build them. But above all, it is not profitable. Large overhead power lines only make sense if the demand for electricity is strong. By definition, small villages do not meet this criterion. By the way, the same goes for telephone lines. The invention of the mobile phone is considered a revolution in our society—in Africa, it has changed people's lives even more dramatically.
There is not enough potential for the creation of value added, ie, the production of goods and services in Africa's widely dispersed villages to justify expensive power lines. It is a vicious circle: without electricity rural areas cannot be developed. In order to break the circle, people need help to help themselves. The solution is affordable solar panels. They can replace the expensive diesel generators which are used in most African villages today.

A trip through Eritrea

A five-week trip through Eritrea has taught me the global and often-overlooked implications of Germany's Energiewende. This country in the northeast of Africa is one of the world's poorest. There, I have seen what clean energy can do. Electricity from solar panels could go a long way to solve the economic and democratic problems of the continent. This was in 1998.
Fred had just finished his studies in the summer of that year. In April we had hired our first employee, so that at least one person would

always be in the office. It was Axel who used to be in charge of my old flat-sharing student dorm in Mainz. He had worked for us for half a year, before becoming a trainee teacher. Since Axel covered our back in the office, I could travel to Eritrea as a wind expert for Lahmeyer International, the planning and consulting company. I worked with engineers and technicians who had already been there for a while. The United Nations had invited tenders for a feasibility study; Lahmeyer had won the contract.

In 1998, I traveled to Eritrea as a wind expert; here I can be seen with my Eritrean colleagues.

At the end of April I arrived in a country on the brink of war with its neighbor, Ethiopia. First air strikes occurred shortly after I had left the country. A few months later, I returned to Eritrea to present the first results of our study. Asmara, the capital, had to observe "security level 1". At night, not one light was allowed to be on. For me, coming from a sheltered country, it was a haunting experience. My generation knows such things only from TV. The fact that several of the colleagues from Eritrea with whom I had travelled were killed in this war was even more depressing. That affected me tremendously, but also convinced me that it is crucial for countries to cut their dependence of finite raw materials.
The five weeks in Eritrea are, to this day, the most impressive experience of my life. We looked at various structures and villages—which systems or combinations were most appropriate? How big should they be? We wanted to come up with exact recommendations: "OK, this village needs so and so many kilowatts of wind power or photovoltaics".

I remember how we drove down the narrow winding and potholed road from Asmara, 2,300 meters up in the mountains, all the time afraid that another car might force us off the road. We honked before each curve signaling that we were coming—but then we drove through the turn at full speed. It was impossible to know whether we were going to hit a boulder, or whether the street had been washed away, or whether the horns of oncoming cars actually worked. The tension was almost unbearable. Later we drove through the desert. Every so often the car got stuck in the sand and we had to dig it out.

Electricity only for the privileged

In Asmara, with its pleasant mountain climate and without mosquitos, we had steak for dinner and slept in comfortable beds. In the villages, mattresses were a rare luxury. Bed frames were totally unfamiliar. Most of the time I slept in my sleeping bag on the floor. At best, such villages had an electricity generator. But only the mayor or the restaurants used it; they were the only ones who could afford diesel fuel. Sometimes there was a TV. In the evenings, women could be seen on the streets of Christian villages, but in the Muslim villages it was men only. I remember one village where thirty or forty men sat in front of a TV. At 8:00 pm the electricity generator was turned off—to save money—and everyone went to sleep.

The food in the villages was simple and scarce. A goat hung on a hook in the shade, but even in the shade the temperature was 30 degrees centigrade, or 86 Fahrenheit. They cut a piece off the goat every day. It was then grilled and placed on a piece of pita bread. It was not really appetizing: after a few days the meat was covered by maggots and flies. On rare occasions a potato or a tomato was added to the dish. In the capital, I had bought a few packet soups. Pea soup was my favorite—the goat was certainly not for me.

The water situation was shocking. In the morning there was one liter for six, seven or eight people. You clean your fingers with it, but only the right hand. Water was too precious for personal hygiene. You eat with the right hand, and with the left you wipe your rear. In one village they didn't even have a diesel generator. We arrived at 11:00 in the morning. For the trip I had bought a watch that displayed the altitude and the temperature. It showed 50 °C (122 °F). The village was 100 meters below sea level. In the afternoon, the temperature reached 59 °C (138 °F). Children played in the sand, without shoes. The soles of their feet had obviously become so hard that they didn't mind.

In the evening we drove to a higher and cooler place, and tried to sleep under some rocks. I looked up and said to a colleague "Hey, the clouds are getting thicker. I think it will rain."
He laughed at me. "You know nothing about the weather here. It never rains."
Two hours later the rain came down.
For several children, it was the first rain they had ever seen.
The next day we came to a village on the coast where people caught fish but had no way to keep them cool. I thought about the goat meat which was rotting in 30 degree heat (86 Fahrenheit). So the task was to produce electricity for certain buildings and appliances, and then for entire villages. For people there it would be a totally different life, with plenty of new opportunities.

Expensive dependency on diesel

Since 1998, the cost of modular technology has fallen by 90 per cent. On the other hand, the price of diesel has tripled. This shows that renewable energy is getting cheaper while the price of fossil fuels continues to increase.

Prices of photovoltaic modules down 68% since 2006

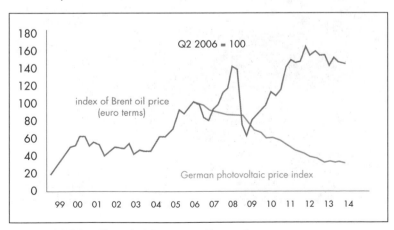

Sources: BSW-Solar—Photovoltaik Preismonitor, Thomson Reuters

In some cases, the cost of photovoltaic sites has been amortized in one or two years, compared to the cost of buying diesel fuel. That is the long-term trend. I had seen the future and what it has in store for us.

But that is not really recognized in Germany. Many still think donating cereals is the best way to help developing countries. It is not.

Renewable energies are one important means to help poor people to help themselves.

We purchase raw materials from Africa; we export to the entire world. And therefore, we can no longer keep the people in an Eritrean village dependent on fossil fuel. Because they burn it, they must continue to buy it—at ever higher prices. This dependence must end.

For the two billion people in rural regions who still do not have access to electricity and no prospects to receive a connection to electricity, a nuclear power plant is no help, nor are coal burning plants or a desert solar project like Desertec.

Most villages cannot be connected to a large power plant which is 300 km (186 miles) away. It would be very expensive—because of the small amounts involved. Prices would be too high for the villagers. Only decentralized solutions make sense.

Villages get their electricity mostly from such diesel generators.

The way villages currently cover their energy needs is not really a sustainable solution. Using diesel generators is so expensive that hardly anyone can afford them. Moreover, the fuel must be transported over long distances on roads that often hardly deserve that name. When the price of oil rises, the transportation becomes too expensive: trucks burn diesel as well. The purchase and installation of a photovoltaic facility with battery storage costs just as much as one year's worth of a generator's diesel consumption. The solar facility would produce electricity for twenty or thirty years—practically at zero cost and independent of transportation costs and the world market price of finite hydrocarbons.

As I said, people need help to help themselves. And that can only work if the cost of the initial investment is very low. Only simple modular solutions will do the trick. Note the global social dimension of Germany's Renewable Energies Law (EEG)—it has been instrumental in making solar technology affordable worldwide.

In 1998 there was already solar technology in Eritrea—but it was not yet affordable.

Costa Rica, a role model for renewables

Today, juwi has subsidiaries in many countries, including Italy, Poland, France, the UK, India, Singapore, South Africa, Chile and the United States. The international expansion actually began with a phone number and a country code on the display which I had never seen before.

I picked up the phone.

The voice at the other end said "Can I speak to the boss?"—"Speaking!" The voice: "Could you put me through to the boss?" "The boss is speaking." There was a pause of a few seconds before the man was convinced that this boss directly answered the phone, rather than being protected by a secretary. It was a German who was calling from Costa Rica. He wanted to become our representative there, and that we should meet.

I said "Interesting, but I can't just simply fly over to Costa Rica." That was in 2000 and we had often received international calls before, from Greece and Turkey for instance, from people who had heard about a project that might be of interest to us. They usually wanted an advance right away even though they had just a lease, but no legal rights and no approvals. But they had already figured out what they should get for their efforts. They wrapped it up in such a clever way that you did not notice right away that their main interest was a commission fee up front, not a reward for an actual order.

The approach of the man from Costa Rica was different. I found him likeable and trustworthy. And so, after reviewing the documents, instead of going on vacation, I flew to San José, the capital of Costa Rica, without speaking a word of Spanish, and met with him. Today juwi Energías Renovables in Costa Rica is not only responsible for that country but for the entire region of central America and the Caribbean.

As a first step we conducted a feasibility study. Such a study should show whether a wind park made sense in a given location, and how it should look like. But we had made a mistake on our application form—we had used a wrong date. Therefore, the project was given to a competitor. But I found the country and the conditions interesting and so we remained active in Costa Rica. I flew there two more times, installed a mast, replaced a wind measurement device 30 meters (98 feet) above ground, without safety belt, and walked to the top of hills which were not accessible by car. I was just very fascinated with Costa Rica. In 2006 we participated in a tender for a 50-megawatt wind park, Planta Eólica Guanacaste.

In order to learn the language, I had hired a Spanish teacher, a Colombian civil engineer by the name of Alejandro who had studied in Germany. Then came the tender, and instead of teaching me Spanish, he helped me with the application. We won. In the meantime, Alejandro has become the Managing Director of juwi Chile. The wind conditions at the project are so good that the 55 turbines are sometimes running non-stop at full capacity for several weeks—they produce enough electricity for 70,000 households.

Ironically, in 2010 we had won the tender to build Costa Rica's first wind park—it was the one for which we had submitted the unsuccessful feasibility study almost a decade ago. The project had been delayed for such a long time because in Latin America the most commonly used word seems to be "mañana"—which literally translated means "tomorrow", but actually stands for "some day".

We managed the wind park project together with two local partners. The park is 1,800 meters high, near Santa Ana, a sort of suburb of the capital San José. It lies in the green mountains of the Central Valley. At that altitude, the wind blows quite strongly: the 17 wind mills produce enough electricity to supply 15,000 households for one entire year.

At the end of 2012, we officially inaugurated the wind park in the presence of Costa Rica's president, Laura Chinchilla. It was obviously an important national project.

For me, the world's most beautiful wind park: Planta Eólica Guanacaste.

Costa Rica has a population of 4.5 million and is about the size of the German state of Niedersachsen (Lower Saxony). The country is a stable democracy and gets along without an army; life expectancy is high. After the first oil crisis, in the seventies, it had decided to switch to renewable energies. Today over 95% of electricity supply comes from regenerative sources. Water accounts for about 80 per cent, geothermal energy and wind contribute about eight per cent each. Costa Rica has excellent wind conditions. Since the eighties, the country has been active in wind energy; it is the pioneer in central America. There are no nuclear power plants.

Costa Rica is a genuine role model for the continent. Other than in neighboring Panama and Nicaragua, the price of electricity is not tied to the price of oil—but the connection still exists to some extent. If it wanted, Costa Rica could easily be on 100 per cent renewables. As it is, they built, ten years ago, when diesel was still inexpensive, large diesel power plants and thus missed the chance to become fully independent of oil. Even though Costa Rica has excellent wind and water resources, rapidly available energy had top priority at the time. Politicians assumed that the oil price would only rise moderately. They probably believed the forecasts of the oil firms. In fact, even back then wind parks would have been a viable alternative: a kilowatt hour of electricity from diesel had cost about the same as one from wind. Today, diesel-generated electricity is three to four times more expensive than wind energy.

That mistake did not make a big difference in Costa Rica because the overall situation is rather good. In Africa, however, the situation is dramatically different. Affordable solar panels should replace expensive diesel generators to supply huts, houses, schools, small industrial parks and townhalls with electricity.

The faster we are able to produce even less expensive solar modules, the sooner new business models will emerge there. Photo voltaic energy provides opportunities to earn money and feed the children. LED lights use considerably less energy than light bulbs; entire huts can be lighted by the power of a single photovoltaic module, replacing those widely-used petroleum lamps which harm people's health. You only notice when you are there how much the lack of electricity and light constrains people's life. In Eritrea, it gets dark all of a sudden shortly after six o'clock. Without artificial light, the day is over.

You cannot, for example, read in the evening. Education stagnates; people cannot get good jobs nor can they develop the country on the basis of their own resources. With solar power you can have refrigerators which keep food fresh or can be used to store medicine. You can pump clean water from deep wells, or charge computers and mobile phones.

Solar energy is a big opportunity for the entire planet—especially for underdeveloped regions. It is of immeasurable social, economic and cultural value.

6

The 100%-vision

I was wrong—a full switch to renewables can be achieved earlier than I thought

For thousands of years, people have recognized that not every corn of a wheat ear should be eaten. Some must be kept as seeds so that we can have wheat in the future as well. The same holds for renewable energies. When we plant something today we will have more in the future. Investments in renewables will bear plenty of fruit.
Politicians like EU Commissioner Günther Oettinger (CDU) always claim that it would not be smart for Germany to switch to clean electricity. It would be too expensive; our industry would be left behind by international competitors and lose market share. In the end, our standard of living would decline, we would be finished.
At first sight it sounds like a valid argument—but in fact it is not. The opposite is true. We have come to a point where Germany is at the cutting edge of the global Energiewende. As I have said before, the country is a role model for the rest of the world. If we continue to focus on developing renewable energies, we will maintain our technological leadership. By exporting our know-how and high-tech goods, we create new jobs and income in Germany. And we benefit from inexpensive electricity in daily life.
Despite all the opposition to the Energiewende, there has been significant progress in at least one respect: it is no longer disputed that it is possible. Today's discussion is about the best way to proceed.
It has been a difficult and long road. In the fall of 1998, I was at a wind energy conference in Wilhelmshaven, a small city on the coast of the North Sea.
I still remember me saying "We will achieve five per cent in five years."
At the time, opponents of wind energy were convinced that wind mills could not produce more than one to two per cent of total electricity supply.

Three young wind energy researchers from Darmstadt actually offered me a bet: that the share of electricity from renewables would actually be less than five per cent five years from now. I accepted. The arguments against electricity from wind were still very powerful.

The mantra of the opposition: where will electricity come from?

A few years later, each of the three researchers sent me a case of (German) champagne!
In spite of all the progress, our society was far from accepting the idea that renewables might one day cover all our electricity needs.
Every time a new coal-burning plant was proposed, the main argument was: "How else can we achieve energy security?"
When the cities of Mainz and Wiesbaden, across from each other on the River Rhine, proposed to build a coal-burning plant, they faced strong popular opposition. Sigmar Gabriel, at the time Minister for the Environment and currently SPD chairman and vice chancellor in the third Merkel government, came to Mainz, defending the project. According to him, "35 per cent from renewables is ok, but where would the other 65 per cent come from?" As mentioned earlier, the coal-burning plant was turned down in the wake of the 2009 local elections—the SPD in Mainz was forced to make a U-turn on the coal issue. Unfazed by this experience, the opposition to renewables continued to stick to its mantra: How can we cover the remaining so and so much per cent of our energy needs?
This number actually became smaller and smaller over time. The Energiewende was on its way.
It was important for me to show that 100 per cent were technically possible and could actually be achieved in the near future. I had thought about it for years, but until 2006 I never mentioned it in public. I was attending a conference organized by Zukunftsinitiative Rheinland-Pfalz (Initiative for the Future) for representatives from science and business. The participants had to sketch out a vision about the energy supply in 2030. For two days, working groups developed various scenarios which were then presented to the plenary audience. I was very disappointed because there were no genuine visions at all. I thought, "No one believes that a quantum leap is possible. We can actually implement their modest projects in two or three years".
I then stepped forward with my group and said, slightly provocatively, that all proposals were nice and fine but not really visionary.

Renewables could actually fully cover our energy needs by 2030. It's technically possible—and we should try it. At the time new coal burning plants were on the drawing boards in Mannheim, in the state of Saarland, near Frankfurt, in Mainz and throughout Germany. It was important for me to show that we did not need coal and nuclear power.

Several people in the audience applauded, but most looked irritated, as if to say, "What is he talking about?" Then someone from the Koblenz Chamber of Industry and Commerce got up and shouted, "These are all dreamers and weirdoes; how can anyone be serious about generating all our electricity from renewables? At most, we can achieve 20% in Rheinland-Pfalz."

I replied that we could do this easily in a few years.

He hopped around like Rumpelstiltskin, ran from his seat to the front and proclaimed "We need safe energy supplies. We need affordable electricity. We don't have enough resources, and therefore we definitely need more conventional power plants."

He added that solar energy could not become profitable anyway and would never be cheaper than electricity from conventional sources. That argument always came up. The discussion went on for a while and became so emotional that we almost got at each other's throats. Today, solar electricity costs half as much as electricity from the socket in the wall.

The fact that people could not at all imagine how the future could look like was very motivating for me. For a long time I had a clear idea of the way forward. Time after time the skeptics had to revise their thinking, always in my direction. Today, in 2014, more than 25% of Germany's electricity supply is from renewables.

A glimpse of the future

Shortly after that conference I was on my way to Costa Rica, and had a stopover in Venezuela. I drove to the beach and spent the entire day there, sketching out how renewables could produce all the electricity that was needed. After ten hours, my feet were terribly sunburned—but I had developed a concept. After my return I produced "The 100% Vision", together with Christian Hinsch, our head of Corporate Communications. The paper was almost one hundred pages long. Our homepage was changed significantly as well.

The concept was published and discussed with local and state-level politicians in Rheinland-Pfalz. We also developed concepts for

Saarland and Hesse, two neighboring German states ("Länder"). At the time, Hermann Scheer, who died in 2010, was the most important political advocate and promoter of renewable energies. He participated in the Hessen state election campaign as a member of Andrea Ypsilanti's shadow government. He had asked me to create a technical feasibility study for a 100 per cent Energiewende—he intended to implement it after they had won the election. It did not happen.

Scheer used parts of the study for his book called "Der energEthische Imperativ." We also cooperated on Carl F. Fechner's film "Energie-autonomie" and exchanged ideas during the shooting. We very much profited from one another. I was fascinated by his intellect, his clear thinking and grand designs. And I hope that he in turn benefited from my pragmatism.

The 100-per cent study shows, no matter what the opponents say, that we do not need millions of wind turbines. In fact, we do not need more than we have today. The paper also shows that there are plenty of suitable areas for wind parks. Only a fraction of those will actually be needed.

The Energiewende is feasible and does not rely on witchcraft. Citizens and local communities can profit from the transition to renewables—not least financially.

In Frankfurt, I had been invited to present the study to the Association of German Engineers (VDI). Afterwards, the traditional question came up first: "What do you do when the wind doesn't blow?" At some point, one of the engineers stood up and wondered whose idea it was to invite a guy like me to speak to them.

I answered calmly that I was glad to be allowed to speak to such an audience, that I was aware that many were skeptical but that at least some in the room would accept my arguments.

At first only two or three applauded—but then the entire room gave me a sustained applause.

Regions become independent

Compared to what I expected in 2006 and 2007, I would use less geothermal energy and more wind today. I have learned that geothermal energy is some distance away from a break-through. By simply repowering old turbines, wind can contribute considerably more to the Energiewende. It is essential, though, that we use wind power always as close as possible to full capacity—this considerably reduces the variability of the generator's output. If the difference between minimum and maximum output is small, the input into the grid is stabilized. In this way storage problems can be avoided. To this day, the feasibility of the Energiewende is seen to depend very much on storage capacities.

Solar energy can also contribute a lot more to electricity supply than I originally thought. In addition, by using the right incentives, consumption can be more closely adjusted to the ups and downs of electricity generation—for instance by linking the supply with heating systems. If there is an oversupply of electricity, it can be used to produce heat—which can be released later.

I thought initially that large storage facilities were indispensable. Knowing what I know today, this is actually less of a problem.

Much of what we worked out in the study is still valid today. The basic message has not changed.

Today many German regions have surpassed the goal of "100 per cent from renewables": they export more electricity than they import. Over 130 counties, regional associations, towns and cities are officially committed to the 100 per cent goal. The trend is up. Our study may have played a small role, something that makes me happy. Rhein-Hunsrück county, in the north of Rheinland-Pfalz, used to import almost its entire energy needs. The county has 103,000 residents and is considered a structurally underdeveloped region—no big industry and therefore not much tax revenue. To produce electricity in the region rather than paying lots of money for importing it is like a "permanent business stimulation program". Bertram Fleck, the district administrator ("Landrat") makes the simple point: "Why give the money to Putin or Saudi-Arabia?" The low mountain ranges of the Hunsrück are perfect for wind power. This year, Fleck expects to produce more than 150% of the energy consumed by the county from renewables and so become an exporter of electricity. Fleck belongs, by the way, to the conservative CDU: energy policies and the regional Energiewende do not depend on where people stand politically.

There is a whole list of committed politicians in the CDU, its sister party CSU and also in the FDP (liberals) who are promoting a faster and decentralized Energiewende, in secret opposition to the official majority opinion of their parties. That is especially true at the local level, but to some extent also at state and federal levels. This is very important. To give an example, the CSU Member of the Bundestag (MP) Josef Göppel is a big supporter of Bavarian energy cooperatives and a critic of the new grand coalition government's energy strategy, especially its attempted move away from decentralized electricity generation; he is one of Germany's most progressive energy politicians.

The Morbach energy landscape

Morbach, a Hunsrück town of 11,000 residents, near Trier, has become a model for regenerative energies. From 1957 to 1995, on a hill above the town, had been the US armed forces' largest weapons arsenal on foreign soil. After the military had left in the mid-nineties, the area of approximately 150 hectares was given back to the town. After several futile attempts to establish commercial, industrial and recreational facilities on the site, the idea of a "Morbach Energy Landscape" was born. Mayor Gregor Eibes (CDU) was the driving force. The integration of power from wind, photovoltaic and biomass was unique at the time.

In the early years of the last decade, 14 wind mills, a photovoltaic facility, a biomass power plant and a wood pellet plant were built on the property—enthusiastically supported by the entire population. In such an environment, it was possible to expand the "energy landscape" in the following years.

By 2020, Morbach wants to be self-sufficient in terms of electricity, heat and mobility, all exclusively generated on the basis of renewables. As to electricity, the town has for some time already covered the annual needs of its households and firms. It earns significant revenues from leasing plots in the "energy landscape" to wind mill operators. These include not only individual investors and the Pfalzwind GmbH but also many citizens from the region who have bought shares in a private limited partnership which invests in wind mills. Morbach's six-digit revenues from those lease contracts are about five per cent of operators' revenues from electricity sales. Another increasingly important source of income for the town is the local business tax ("Gewerbesteuer").

Morbach has thus improved its fiscal situation by strongly backing renewable energy. The population is wholeheartedly behind the project. Since the Morbach Energy Landscape is a role model for the Energiewende, it attracts thousands of visitors each year. Tourism has therefore become another source of income for the town.

I cite these examples in some detail because other German counties, towns and cities can learn from them. When local decision makers are thinking about renewables, they should be aware of the following positive aspects: low and stable electricity prices, security of supply, investments in a technology that has a bright future, and new jobs. All this strengthens the regional economy and creates new opportunities, especially for people in rural areas.

Keeping the money in town

Another example is the Wörrstadt association of municipalities ("Verbandsgemeinde"). Juwi's headquarters are there. By 2017, the town and the surrounding villages plan to cover their entire energy needs from renewable sources. The "Verbandsgemeinde" with its 30,000 residents is the first German municipality which buys its wind electricity directly from the producer; it is a juwi pilot project. Mayor Markus Conrad (CDU) has acquired a wind mill for the community. It generates six million kilowatt hours of electricity per year, more than enough for the needs of the town's public properties. The rest is sold. The local government also leases the roofs of the school gym and the elementary school to operators of photovoltaic facilities. Here again, the idea is to keep the money in the community, and/or generate additional revenues. Wörrstadt has been betting on renewables since 2007. Ernst Walter Görisch (SPD), "Landrat" of the Alzey-Worms county of which Wörrstadt is a part, also supports this policy.

In the second half of the 2000s the main issue was still about explaining that the Energiewende was feasible. In order to get attention, I had organized events, given presentations—and had also created several fashion accessories around the 100 per cent topic.

In 2009 the Business Juniors of the Chamber of Commerce had awarded us a prize which I was going to accept. Now, we had T-shirts with "100%" logos, but the event was a ball where men were expected to wear suits. Since I wanted to convey our message visually at the occasion, an orange-colored tie was produced, with the embroidered inscription "100 per cent renewable" which attracted quite some attention. The tie became sort of famous under the name "the 100 per cent tie" and was imitated by others, for instance by "Landrat" Bertram Fleck of the Rhein-Hunsrück county in his campaign for the expansion of renewables. He actually went one step further and created a "100-plus tie".

It may sound banal, but the tie was a conversation piece for several years. It helped to start discussions about the potential of renewable energies—including discussions with the state's premier minister.

Kurt Beck—at the time prime minister of Rheinland-Pfalz—was visibly impressed by the 100% vision.

A tie as a conversation piece

Two or three weeks later Kurt Beck, the boss of the state's government in Mainz, came to see us at Schneebergerhof. He was on a press tour through the "Land" and we were giving him a tour of the wind and photovoltaic sites near our farm. As always at such occasions, I wore my 100 per cent tie. When the journalists asked what it meant, I was happy to explain it to them. They then turned to Kurt Beck: was he also in favor of 100 per cent by 2030?

74

Beck smiled and said that the switch to renewables could not be so fast. Coal and gas were still needed. But he also said, "We need young people who have visions of the future."
Anyhow, the tie had kicked off the discussion of my favorite topic. Just two years later—after the Fukushima catastrophe and the 2011 state elections in Rheinland-Pfalz which led to an SPD-Green coalition government—"100 per cent renewables by 2030" had become an official policy goal. The state was determined to do what it could to help limiting the increase of the global temperature to 2 °C. To achieve that, global CO_2 emissions had to be reduced by 90 per cent between 1990 and 2050, and by 40 per cent between 1990 and 2020. The coalition contract banned the construction of coal-burning power plants.
The state has a strong incentive to become a net exporter of electricity and to promote the economy in all its regions—and across all party programs. The incentive is so strong that the goal could be reached even earlier. In terms of wind power, of the states not bordering the ocean, Rheinland-Pfalz is ahead of the other "Länder". The aim is to increase wind power capacity by a factor of five by 2020. According to the Ministry of the Economy, Climate Protection and Energy, the "state actively supports the process of decentralizing energy supplies."
When I give a speech today, I say, "Ladies and gentlemen, I must admit, I have been wrong about the dynamics of the Energiewende".
I was not wrong about the 100 per cent goal, but about the time line. The transition could come earlier than I thought. I did not expect that opinions would be revised so quickly, certainly not at the time when I gave my impassionate speech at the "vision" workshop. The "Land" Schleswig-Holstein which borders on both the North Sea and the Baltic Sea, wants to achieve 100 per cent by 2020.
The Rheinland-Pfalz government coalition contract of 2011 was like a dream come true for me. That is why it is quite sobering to watch the new Merkel government procrastinate on the Energiewende issue.
My dream is not only about the generation of clean electricity. There are many small components which are also important: we must, for instance, change the way we travel. The car must be reinvented.

7

The reinvention of the car

Why renewable energy is also needed for our mobility

In 2007, I saw my first Tesla in California. It was the roadster which hit the market that year—the first lithium ion battery powered all-electric sports car with a range of over 300 kilometers (186 miles). I was at an Eco-Solar trade show in San Francisco and used the opportunity to visit the photovoltaic module manufacturer Nanosolar; their headquarters is in San Jose, at the southernmost point of the San Francisco Bay. The headquarters of Tesla is in Palo Alto which is on the way from San Francisco to San Jose. And so I took a detour to Tesla and was immediately fascinated by the car. When Tesla opened a showroom in July 2008, five minutes from the city center of Palo Alto and the renowned Stanford University, I was invited. On this occasion, I met Elon Musk.

He was born in 1971 and founded Tesla in 2003. Prior to that, he had developed an online payment system. His company later merged with PayPal and was sold at the beginning of the last decade to eBay for 1.5 billion dollars. Musk's share was 11.7 per cent or 175 million dollars. With that money, he founded three firms: an aerospace company, a solar company which produces and installs solar panels—and Tesla.

I got to know Musk as a fast, restive and competent guy.

I found him both fascinating and fundamentally different from me. In typical American style, Musk launches companies in order to sell them for as much money as possible. I am not interested in that. I also would not start a rocket company in order to develop space tourism for the superrich. I don't think the world is really waiting for that.

At the event in Palo Alto I asked Musk whether I could buy a car from him. He said, "That's not possible."

The Teslas were not yet ready for delivery and had a long waiting list.

I asked, "How many cars have you sold in Europe so far?"

He answered, "For the moment, our goal is two hundred and fifty. One hundred have already been sold."

I said, "I will buy another ten, Elon, if you give me one right away." So the deal was done and I actually received a Tesla Roadster within a month.

It was the first Tesla in Germany, and it was orange.

We sold the other ten Teslas, which arrived later, but kept the orange one.

I do not need a sports car as a status symbol.

But I have been convinced for a long time that sensible mobility can only be electric, because it is considerably more efficient than mobility based on internal combustion engines. And it fits in with my campaign for renewable energy. In 2002, I had already bought an electrically powered soapbox—to show that electro-mobility is the future.

The "car" was a City EL, a light three-wheel thing for one person, with a top speed of 60 kilometers (37 miles) per hour. I drove around Mainz with it. Especially small children were excited about it. You can put it in a bicycle parking space and it does not make any noise—which made it also interesting for adults. Later I switched to a Twike. It runs on batteries as well and has also three wheels, but it seats two people. Both "cars" are not suitable for the mass market, though.

When a genuine electric car was finally introduced, I was ready to buy one.

The most fascinating thing about the Tesla: its batteries provide power for a range of 300 kilometers.

My idea was to make a statement about the future of mobility and show people that there was an alternative to their gas guzzlers.

For this reason I also drove a Tesla Model S for a few months, right after it had been launched in the US. It has a range of almost 500 kilometers (311 miles). The Tesla S is a five-seat limousine, also powered by lithium-ion batteries. Compared to the other e-cars which have to be recharged after 60 to 150 kilometers (37 and 93 miles), it is a genuine breakthrough.

The Tesla is still very heavy and very expensive. If you drive cautiously, today's e-cars consume 10 to 20 kilowatt hours per 100 kilometers (62 miles), presently the equivalent of 2.50 euros to 5.00 euros. Modern cars with internal combustion engines need 5 to 8 liters of fuel for the same distance, ie 7.50 euros to 12.00 euros. It can be expected that by optimizing weight and aerodynamics, electricity consumption can be cut to 5 to 10 kilowatt hours. A Nissan Leaf stores 24 kilowatt hours at the moment, a Mercedes A-Class E-Cell 36 kilowatt hours, and the Tesla about 56 kilowatt hours. The battery of a Tesla weighs about 440 kilograms (970 pounds).

It is realistic that within five to ten years batteries with the same capacity will weigh only 35 per cent of what they weigh in 2014. Because the electric engine is much lighter than a combustion engine, tomorrow's e-car will be lighter than a gasoline car today. Assuming a consumption of 5 kilowatt hours per 100 kilometers , one could therefore drive 1,000 kilometers (621 miles). So the range will be less of an issue in the future.

Kilometers before re-charging, various models

Source: VCD car environment list 2012/2013; manufacturers' specifications

Why is that so important? For a full-scale Energiewende, we not only need electricity from renewables, but heating and moving around must change as well. Mobility accounts for almost 30 per cent of our entire energy consumption, and so far it largely depends on fossil fuels. In the future, these fuels will be much more expensive and will be needed for more important things than powering cars. In addition, it can be expected that society will gradually move toward zero emissions of CO_2 and other dangerous substances.

Electro mobility is capable of much more. It will be an important and affordable building block for the storage of renewable energies. It will help to stabilize the electricity grid which one day will be connected to millions of e-cars. When too much electricity is produced, the car batteries can be used for storage; when electricity demand exceeds supply, power can be drawn from the cars. These buffers will play a very important role.

The previous conservative-liberal German government had decided that by 2020 one million electric cars should be on the streets. But there has been almost no political support so far. The public is still convinced that e-cars are too expensive, are not suited for longer distances, and take too long to re-charge. It is true: the Tesla is too expensive for the mass market. But the issue is now to press ahead technologically to produce better and less expensive cars and batteries. As is well known, 95 per cent of all cars are not driven more than 100 kilometers a day. So 95 per cent of all trips could already be made with an electric car today (if initial outlays for the purchase of such a car were a lot less than today).

At juwi we are progressively replacing our company fleet of about one hundred cars by electric models from various manufacturers.

Because our company stands for a sustainable mix of energy from various renewables and also for electro-mobility, I had been invited to the German government's "Summit on Electro-Mobility". Following that, I have met, on several occasions, chancellor Merkel, her ministers and board members of Deutsche Bahn, Siemens, BMW, Audi, Mercedes and VW. When Dieter Zetsche or Martin Winterkorn, the CEOs of Mercedes and VW, claimed that in the foreseeable future there would be no electric cars in Germany with a range of more than 100 or 150 kilometers , I said, "Yes, there are. I am driving one."

But there is progress: in the fall of 2013, we could finally add German cars to our fleet. I have already switched to a BMW i3. It is produced in east Germany and thus good for our economy. It is made of aluminum and plastic, reinforced with carbon fibers, which considerably reduces its weight. It has little road resistance and good aerodynamics. BMW has recognized that electro-mobility is the way ahead. The firm wants to set new standards.

While we wait for the considerably lighter and better cars of the future, we must use today's technology to increase operating ranges. One of the simplest methods is to install either a larger or an additional battery. But this increases the weight of the car. The alternative is to install a so-called range extender. The Opel Ampera is such a car—it is now part of the juwi fleet. Its electric engine is good for a range of 87 kilometers (54 miles).

My fellow board member, Martin, drives the Ampera two times 50 kilometers (31 miles) every day, from Frankfurt to work in Wörrstadt and back. He does not need the range extender for these trips because there are charging stations both at his home and at work. For longer distances, the Ampera has a gas-powered onboard generator which produces electricity. The range of the car is over 500 kilometers.

The Ampera is considerably better than the classic hybrid models which are de facto gasoline-powered cars with an electric boost when starting. But it has two engines. The combustion engine is still needed—for longer distances.

The new BMW i3 stands for a quantum leap in electro mobility. It is a pure electric car—the wheels are all the time powered by the electric engine. As an option, a range extender in the form of a small and light Otto-engine (in the future a fuel cell) can be installed—it produces electricity which keeps the battery charge condition constant. In winter, the excess heat from the combustion engine can be used to heat the car. The fuel tank holds just a few liters. In the future, it should become possible to easily install and remove such a system in which case the range extender could deliver both electricity and heat for a house, especially in winter.

The 2013 edition of the Renault Zoe uses a heat pump to warm the passenger cabin; even in winter it has a range of 100 kilometers. In more than one respect this small electric car is very impressive. It costs 21,700 euros; its intelligent battery charger is compatible with household electricity and quick charging stations. The battery can be rented for only 79 euros a month. Another possibility is the so-called quick-charging system. Tesla for example is using it.

I expect that all these systems will soon be replaced by considerably better solutions.

The quality of the battery will be dramatically improved. In a few years, electric cars will have batteries which are not heavier than today but have twice as much power. But one does not have to wait for this to happen—the electric cars that are on the market today can already be used for everyday driving. The more cars are bought, the faster will be the technological progress. It is important to create a strong momentum.

This is key. One question that is always asked—how do you charge the batteries if you live on the fourth floor of an apartment house in a big city. It is, of course, a legitimate question; but it is often asked by those who want to slow down e-mobility. It is, in fact, a rather difficult issue, but not the most critical one. The necessary momentum will initially come from two groups: homeowners and companies with fleets of cars. If you fill up the battery at home and at work, like my colleague Martin, you cover already something like 90 per cent of your total needs. He does not have to worry about charging stations.

For sure, with rising numbers of electric cars on the road, there must be many charging stations, preferably in places where electric cars are parked for several hours and where the electricity comes directly from renewables. Think rest stops on motorways or shopping centers. That is the next step. It is important that the new infrastructure includes access to "green" power stations such as wind mills and that the charging time is reduced. Battery-changing services are an alternative.

In this way, clean electricity can directly be fed into electric cars. The underlying infrastructure such as electric cables or telephone lines can be jointly used to construct and operate profitable charging stations.

At home I charge my battery with an extension cable—the source of energy is my 15-kilowatt photovoltaic panel on the roof. Solar electricity is not always available. But it is already possible today to install a micro combined heat and power unit (CHP) in the basement which produces clean electricity around the clock. I burn pellets for heating, but so far there are no reliable CHPs that use pellets for heating and electricity. We are working on a project to generate electricity from heat at your home. In two years we will be there.

Charging batteries with electricity that comes exclusively from renewables is already possible at juwi. Our head office is connected to wind power and solar energy; we have a block heating and power unit that uses bio mass. In this way, we do not need electricity from the outside: 100 per cent of our electricity comes from renewables. We have developed a company carport with solar cells on the roof. These produce enough electricity for 12,000 kilometers (7,456 miles) per parking space per year. Our electric cars park directly underneath the solar panels.

In the end, one aspect is all-important: we need a comprehensive approach. E-mobility only makes sense if the share of renewables in electricity production continues to rise, if additional cars do not mean burning even more coal than today. Driving electric cars is cheap. One wind mill is enough for 12,000, and 160 large wind mills are enough for one million electric and hybrid cars. Just by installing more efficient heating pumps in homes, Germany could save electricity for two million electric cars.

One thing is certain: electro mobility will not fail because there is not enough of renewable energy. In 2011, Germany consumed the equivalent of 714 terawatt hours for gasoline and diesel powered vehicles. A switch to electric cars would save two-thirds of that. Lighter and more aerodynamic cars will cut the number in half again.

The new Very Light Car (VLC) of the US company Edison 2—it is very light and streamlined and thus extremely energy efficient.

Mobility soon too expensive

There are two other key arguments for electro mobility. First: the price of oil-based fuels. No one knows what the future will bring, and all scenarios depend on assumptions. Since the oil price has quadrupled in the past ten years, one plausible assumption is that it will continue to increase. In the medium term, a barrel of oil may cost more than 200 dollars. Burning oil does not only destroy the environment, it will also be too expensive for driving. It is a scarce resource. Second: we need oil for more important things. At some point, driving electric cars will not only be better for the climate, it will also be less expensive. As I have shown above, the electricity for 100 kilometers in an electric car costs somewhere between 2.50 euros and 5.00 euros today. If a combustion engine burns seven liters per 100k, we currently have to pay more than 10 euros. Switching to renewables means the price of electricity will remain constant, or fall (because of economies of scale). On the other hand, the price of gasoline will definitely rise in the long run.

Constructing an electric engine is not particularly difficult. But the carmakers have invested fortunes into the development and production of gasoline and diesel motors—it is understandable that they want to use these investments for as long as they can. Germany is one of a few countries which does not promote electro mobility, presumably because the world-beating car manufacturers need protection: they would lose a lot of revenue if the switch to electro mobility came too fast. This is why the industry, the country's largest, keeps telling us that electric engines are only useful and feasible for short distances. Tesla is de facto the only manufacturer that has built a luxury electric car, the Tesla S—probably because it produces nothing but electric cars.

If we genuinely want progress, we will get it—my experience with wind and solar energy has taught me that. Tesla is another example. The firm had never considered to invest in old technology: so now we have an electric car for every-day use which can compete with traditional luxury models in terms of comfort.

Electro mobility, based 100 per cent on renewables, is not only possible but will be an important element of energy production that is 100 per cent "clean". Inevitably, electro mobility will become enormously important for the labor market. The status symbol of today's youth is the smartphone and not the car anymore. Twenty years ago, people defined themselves via the cars they drove. Our mentality has changed, just as technology and our daily life have changed. We do things today which are actually crazy. People are gradually recognizing this—and will re-order their priorities.

An example: at the airport in Munich you can now share taxis. Until a short while ago, one person per taxi was considered normal even when ten other people had inner city destinations within a radius of 500 meters. Today after landing, you enter your destination on an internet platform and usually find one or two others to share a taxi. This is an ideal solution for traffic, environmental and resource efficiency problems—and for the customers: they have practically no major inconvenience and often pay only a third of the usual price.

Mobility of the future: the Autro

In a few years we will organize our mobility with a smart armband. You tell your device "I want to go to the airport in five minutes." The app finds out whether and where there are other people in the neighborhood who also have to go to the airport. A car will automatically pull up whose size depends on the number of passengers. If you are alone, it will no longer be a large taxi; expect a small car for just one passenger. Payment will be via direct debit.

I call it the automatic transportation, or "Autro".

We no longer need individually owned cars to satisfy individual wishes and needs. The Autro adjusts to individual needs—from music to the color of the paint. The moment the smart armband connects with the car, it loads your preferred music, adjusts to the temperature you like and changes to the desired color. The Autro does not need a driver—it moves automatically.

The future is here already. In California's Silicon Valley, Google has been working on the Autro concept for several years. California's governor, Jerry Brown, decided in 2012 that the Autros may be tested on public roads. "We will witness how science fiction turns into tomorrow's reality", said the governor. He suspected that people would initially be somewhat nervous when they saw an Autro drive by. But they would quickly get used to it.

Such cars will actually increase both the security and the speed of driving—because they will make fewer mistakes than humans. The Autros can move on rails or on roads. Berlin—Hamburg, for instance, would probably be a rail route where several Autros are linked to each other.

If the destination is not in a high-speed corridor but in a remote place, you can drive on the street, as today.

In the future, we do not need so many automobiles—they are standing idle for most of the time anyway. Instead, we will use Autros which are better adapted to our needs. If you want to take your surfboard to the island of Rügen on the Baltic Sea, an appropriate Autro will arrive at your place. Mobility will become less expensive because it adjusts to what people actually need.

Today "my" car, parked in front of the house or in the garage, is a rather inflexible thing. Its full capacity is only used a few times per year, for example, when four people want to go to the same destination, or on vacation when the large trunk is actually needed. In the future, if you want to go on vacation in Italy, 800 kilometers away, a "made-to-measure" car will arrive within five minutes in front of your house.

Many people who are planning a vacation are scared off by the complicated process of booking a rental car. In the future, you just tell your smart armband. Once we are confident about the comfort and security of the new technology, owning a car will no longer be important. The new type of mobility will be the new normal, mostly because it is clearly superior.

The two main features of the Autro are its advanced aerodynamics and its low weight. Compared to today's electric cars, it will have a considerably larger range—thanks to batteries which are two to three times lighter than today and solar cells which are three times more efficient. The Autros of the future will be very light and very inexpensive—especially when they are manufactured in large quantities. Since electricity from wind and sun will always be affordable, the marginal cost per kilometer is close to zero. Driving one thousand kilometers for five euros will not be a problem. That is exactly the reason why new-age electric cars will be accepted in the market place. They are simply unbeatably cheap.

Whether it will take fifteen or thirty years to get there, I do not know. But I do know that it is the future.

8

The battle of the systems

Two ways to produce energy

Energy is a huge market. According to business magazine *Fortune,* in 2013 seven of the world's ten biggest corporations by sales were in oil (6) and electricity (1). Two of the leading oil companies are from China, two from Britain and one each from the US and France. The world's largest electricity firm is China's State Grid.

Rank ▼	Company	Revenues ($ b)	Profits ($ b)
1	Royal Dutch Shell	481.7	26.6
2	Wal-Mart Stores	469.2	17.0
3	Exxon Mobil	449.9	44.9
4	Sinopec Group	428.2	8.2
5	China National Petroleum	408.6	18.2
6	BP	388.3	11.6
7	State Grid	298.4	12.3
8	Toyota Motor	265.7	11.6
9	Volkswagen	247.6	27.9
10	Total	234.3	13.7

World's largest companies in 2013, by revenues

In Germany four large utilities are dominating the electricity market: E.on, RWE, Vattenfall and EnBW. Their aim is to maintain market control. Each of them operates a few large, often highly subsidized power stations which use brown and black coal, gas and uranium as inputs. They are the old system. Since they have split up the German market into four segments and do not compete much with each other, they are actually four regional monopolists. They used to be very cash rich; they still wield enormous power.

On the other hand there is the new system of decentralized electricity generation which relies on small units powered by "clean" renewables, ie, wind, sun, water, biomass and geothermal heat. Each kilowatt-hour of electricity produced by photovoltaic facilities on people's roofs is in competition with the Big 4 and reduces their revenues and profits.

Priorities of the big players

It is simple: their goal is to maximize profits for their mainly anonymous national and international shareholders, including investment funds. Everything else is of secondary importance. This means the utilities have a strong incentive to maintain the old system with its large power plants and electricity grids. It is in their interest to keep households dependent on their products and services.

The executives of such firms report to boards of directors which in turn represent the shareholders. These shareholders want financial returns—and immediately, please. Management usually tries to run their large power plants at full capacity. That is the most profitable short-term strategy. Capital spending and investing to renovate existing plants—and thus doing something for the future—is less of a priority. Moreover, there is a conflict of interest: if a utility builds a large wind park, ie, starts a new business, it would accelerate the decline of its profitable old business model of burning fossil fuels. In business school jargon this is called cannibalization.

I am therefore not at all surprised that the managers and the board members of the utilities do not want to switch to renewables if they can avoid it. Despite the deterioration of the climate and the environment, the approaching end of the fossil age and the unstoppable momentum of the Energiewende, they fight toes and nails to postpone the moment of truth. What else would you expect? The perfidious thing is that they do not fight openly but let others do it: politicians, their lobbyists, some media, or initiatives of activists against wind energy.

How do the big utilities play the game?

From early on, their main strategy has been to discredit electricity from renewables. For years, the German energy establishment had claimed that the Energiewende would not be feasible. At first, the industry asserted that renewables could at most cover one per cent of electricity consumption, then this was changed to two, then five— in ads, these "forecasts" were presented to the German public as sort of scientific. Later the establishment claimed that electricity generation from renewables was too slow—electricity supply could not be guaranteed unless the big utilities were allowed to build conventional power plants. If not, there might be brown-outs and other catastrophes.

Renewables now account for more than 25 per cent of electricity generation. Since 2005, the share has more than doubled. The arguments of the establishment have been disproved by hard facts: "clean" energy generation works, and it is expanding fast. Therefore, the utilities have come up with a third argument. They now say: the Energiewende is much too fast. In Berlin, the grand coalition of CDU/CSU and SPD has more or less bought that argument. Fortunately, some of the "Länder" continue to have a different perspective. In Rheinland-Pfalz and Hessen, where the Greens are represented in coalition governments, politicians are not willing to sign the death certificate of the Energiewende. They realize that a full implementation of Sigmar Gabriel's „corner stone paper" would mean the end of the expansion of onshore wind power.

Who is supporting the electricity establishment?

Lobbyists who put pressure on politicians, politicians who let themselves be impressed, media which buy their arguments and spread them, the "Initiative Neue Soziale Marktwirtschaft" INSM (New Social Market Economy) and the DIHK, the umbrella organization of Germany's chambers of industry and commerce—which claims to speak for big electricity producers and large consumers of electricity. And many others.

Politicians who fight for the interests of large utilities exist in all parties and parliaments, including for some time now in the European parliament in Brussels. But no one can claim any longer that the Energiewende is impossible. After all, the European Union has decided that 80 per cent of electricity must come from renewables by 2050. Therefore, the rearguard action of the energy establishment consists of slowing down the Energiewende. They have also been looking for new arguments.

In April 2013, they found one. The conservative-liberal majority of the European parliament rejected the reform of the emissions trading system; Philipp Rösler (FDP, liberal), Germany's Minister of the Economy at the time, applauded. The reason he liked the outcome of the vote is that he was afraid that Europe might otherwise be de-industrialized. The EU economy is supposedly at risk if the financial burden of firms becomes even heavier: paying for expensive CO_2 certificates would be just too much. A very broad alliance had been at work, across party lines: aside from Rösler, the EU Energy Commissioner Günther Oettinger (CDU), Nordrhein Westfalen's state premier Hannelore Kraft (SPD) and others had joined forces to defend the interests of the coal industry. A "dirty alliance of the fossil fuel comrades", as it was put in a comment of the online magazine tagesschau.de.

Carbon dioxide emissions
million tons of carbon dioxide

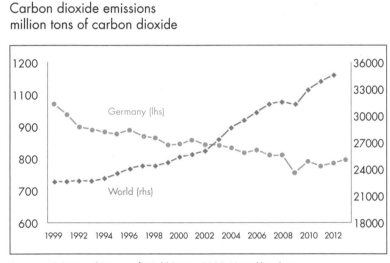

Sources: BP Statistical Review of World Energy 2013, Umweltbundesamt

A reformed trading system could have become an important European tool for reducing CO_2 emissions. It will now take longer.
The status quo is in the interest of large industrial firms and utilities which can continue to damage the climate, especially the operators of coal-burning power plants—since they do not pay for the damage they cause, they are effectively subsidized by society. If the price of CO_2 certificates collapses, as has happened in the past, the price of electricity at the electricity exchange will also fall—

whereupon the EEG-levy, absurd as it is, rises and gas powered plants have no chance: their costs are suddenly too high relative to coal-powered plants. EEG stands for Erneuerbare Energien Gesetz, or renewable energy law. If readers find this strange—it is. Here is another explanation: if the prices at the electricity exchange fall—because of a surplus supply of electricity from renewables—the EEG-levy goes up. It is the difference between the government-guaranteed feed-in tariffs for "renewable" electricity and the free-market price at the electricity exchange. On the other hand, low and falling prices of CO_2 certificates, ie, permits for pollution, make old coal-burning power plants competitive relative to modern but expensive gas-fired stations. The negative effects on CO_2 emissions are obvious.

There was only one winner: coal. The rest loses.

Also, even though the big energy producers are well-connected to all German parties, it is not exaggerated to over-emphasize the special role of the FDP (liberal party) which has acted as a kind of representative of big industry in previous federal governments. In some states where the party is still in government, it continues to play that role—which is a bit ironic because its constituency is actually the middle class. But there is an anti-middle class and anti-citizen faction in the FDP, which goes all the way back from Philipp Rösler and Rainer Brüderle, the last FDP ministers for the economy in the federal government, to the nineties.

I recall my first meeting with Rainer Brüderle who used to be the minister for the economy in Rheinland-Pfalz, the home state of juwi. He was also the chairman of the regional FDP. It was 1997, and we had spoken with a representative of the FDP about wind power. He had a plot of land that was interesting for us. He told us that "young, dynamic entrepreneurs like you will surely interest Mr Brüderle; I will bring you together; it will be great."

We then met at a regional party convention—where Brüderle talked like a coal and nuclear lobbyist, saying that one wind mill was nice to have, but more were not needed, they were useless.

So so.

That was the typical argument of the energy establishment in the nineties: "Of what use are two or three wind mills?", followed by my favorite homily "what will we do when the wind doesn't blow?"

To top it off, he said: "Besides, wind power can only be an additive source of electricity. For physical reasons, the grid can at most accommodate an additional five per cent anyway."

That was for me like a penalty kick: "Dear Mr. Brüderle, as a physicist, I would be pleased if I could explain to you why it is possible to feed much more than 5% into our grids." After first sporting a big grin, he wanted to change the topic. When I insisted that we should continue the discussion of the issue he became surly and declared that he was done with the topic. It was very embarrassing for his FDP colleague who had brought us to the event. What I found embarrassing was Brüderle's lack of competence. That was the first and last time Brüderle was willing to talk to me. Since 1997 he has not visited us once, although we had invited him to juwi many times. The entire leadership of the state's FDP has come to see us. He has not.

Directly after Peter Altmaier had become federal minister of the environment in 2012, Brüderle publicly stated that changing to renewables was actually more difficult and expensive than had been thought. We would need more coal-burning power stations. And in the summer of 2013, he asked again for a moratorium for wind and sun. Great idea. Most of the mid-sized firms which support the FDP will probably survive that.

Why is the FDP in bed with the large utilities, and the big boys in general? For strategic reasons, I am afraid. The liberal FDP has almost the same constituency as the Greens in terms of education and income. For the Liberals, fighting for big energy is therefore an important differentiating factor. Because the Greens stand for renewable energies, the FDP must take exactly the opposite position. That is why it supports the energy establishment, even though most of the party's voters are middle class. Energy policies are the exception; in this regard the FDP is the party of the large players.

But even the Greens sometimes sing the songs of the large utilities. They like offshore electricity and rave about the jobs that come with it. As it is, offshore wind projects are so expensive that they can only be handled by giant cash-rich firms; they are not suited for small-scale decentralized electricity generation and the involvement of households and local communities! I expect more from the Greens—they must fight for a decentralized Energiewende, ie for the participation of people on the ground.

And what about the chambers of industry and commerce? In my view, they take their cues from big industry and have often not looked seriously at the material about renewables that was given to them—they tried to avoid the issue because they might have arrived at different conclusions.

The "Initiative New Social Market Economy" is yet another matter. The INSM is a lobby of the metal industry's employers' association ("Arbeitgeberverband Gesamtmetall") and the energy-intensive industry. In 2012, Wolfgang Clement, the former "Superminister" in Gerhard Schröder's SPD/FDP government, became its chairman—he had been an opponent of renewables since his time as SPD state premier of Nordrhein-Westfalen. The state is the home of E.on and RWE and most of Germany's heavy industry. He once said that the Energiewende was a state interventionist activity based on comprehensive subsidies. As minister of the economy in Berlin, he worried that the Energiewende might slow economic growth—and was actually a trillion euro mistake.

During the 2008 state election campaign, he had come out against Andrea Ypsilanti, the SPD's candidate for state premier, because the Energiewende was a key plank of her election platform. He is clearly the right guy for the INSM whose message is to "stop the EEG (law)—otherwise the Energiewende will fail".

Basically the argument is always the same: compatibility of energy production with the environment? All well and fine, but not at the expense of social welfare and energy security!

Manuel Frondel, a professor at the Rheinisch-Westfälisches Institut für Wirtschaftsforschung in Essen (RWI, an economic think tank) can always be relied upon to come up with ludicrous numbers and arguments against the Energiewende. Whenever the enemy is renewables, especially solar electricity, Frondel is there, comparing the (enormous) costs with the (non-existent) positive effects. He will reliably conclude that switching to renewables leads to "an avalanche of costs" and is thus "a risk for growth and the standard of living". Not to mention that it puts us on the road to a communist-like command economy.

What is motivating this guy? The moderator of "Monitor", a Channel 1 TV-show, once asked him about the sponsor of one of his studies which had denounced solar electricity as unnecessarily expensive. The first answer was that there was no sponsor. When the journalist provided evidence that there actually was one, he said the sponsor was an "independent energy research institute." When "Monitor" then pointed out that this "Institute for Energy Research" was a lobby, funded by oil and coal companies, Frondel said "we were not really aware of this." He tried to convey the impression that forgetting to mention the paymaster of his study was regrettable, but nothing serious. Thus are the standards of economic research at the RWI!

Battle of the systems

issue	"old energy"	"new energy"
number of stations	a few large power plants	many decentralized power plants
ownership structure	a few oligopolists, many, mostly anonymous shareholders, both domestic and from abroad	many regional players (citizens, farmers, local communities)
motivation	to maximize profits	protection of the environment, keep the revenues in the region
cross subsidies	traffic, waste management, telecom	hardly any or none
state subsidies	for decades, very high (research, waste disposal, implementation, operations)	modest (directly for research/indirectly as a result of the EEG law)
"sustainability triangle"	profits for the large players, safe electricity supply, benefits for the environment	1. improvement of the environment 2. profitability 3. safe energy supply
powered by …	coal/nuclear/gas/ offshore wind	wind/sun/bio mass
beneficiaries	a few, eg, international investment funds	many households and small regional players
the losers	locally: emissions and destruction of nature, caused by strip mining; globally: climate change, emissions, destruction of nature, plundering of reserves	locally: the landscape
politics	considerable expenses for lobbying, long-standing relationships, rewards in the form of board seats ("jobs for the boys")	not too close yet, but lobbying is intensifying
jobs	approximately 200,000	approximately 400,000

issue	"old energy"	"new energy"
industry cooperation with ...	big industry, such as chemicals, metal processing, shipyards	the crafts, manufacturers of wind mills and PV panels
price setting	seemingly low production costs: but important costs such as damaging the environment are externalized (born by the public in the form of taxes and higher insurance premiums)	seemingly expensive, but all social costs are included in the price of electricity
dependent on ...	finite resources, raw material imports, a small number of companies	weather conditions (wind, sun)
cost of transporting raw materials and electricity	high/extraction of coal, gas and uranium and their transformation occur at different places/separation of production and consumption	production close to resources and consumers
long-term perspectives	poor: finite resources, rising costs	good: unlimited resources, decreasing costs

The early stages of the battle

In order to understand how the battle of the systems is fought, it helps to look, in chronological order, at the arguments used by the old system to prevent or slow down the Energiewende. Right from the start, the strategy of the establishment was to hide its business interests behind scientific, political, social and even conservationist arguments. The goal has always been—and still is today—to stoke fears of the new and unknown and thus create mental blocks.

In the early years, the prime target was wind energy, the "wind mill delusion". "Old energy" instrumentalized landscape conservationists who have either financial or romantic motives.

The photovoltaic boom began sometime around 2005, followed, in short order, by a massive propaganda campaign of the opponents. One of the main proponents was, once again, the RWI think tank in

Essen. RWI is not RWE, the big utility, but both use the same arguments. Their aim was to point out the downside of solar energy. Jürgen Grossmann, chairman of RWE, likened it to growing pineapples in Alaska. The message was that sun power did not make economic sense in cloudy Germany. After years of bombarding the public in this way, the energy establishment succeeded—the feed-in tariffs paid to the owners of solar panels were cut so much that this "clean" energy lost much of its economic appeal. Many German photovoltaic companies and producers of modules went bankrupt. The large utilities had won a battle, but not the war. They began to panic again when—following the solar boom and the nuclear catastrophe in Fukushima (March 11, 2011)—politicians in the southern states of Bavaria and Baden-Württemberg decided to allow wind parks on their territories.

Renewable energies in the hands of the people
– ownership structure of renewable electricity capacity in Germany (2012) –

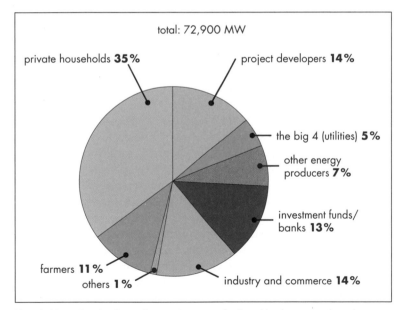

Households, project developers, farmers, investment funds and banks are now the main owners of installed renewable energy capacity; the big 4 utilities play only a minor role.
Source: Agentur für Erneuerbare Energien

While the old energy establishment had successfully lobbied against renewables for many many years, they do not really know what to make of the new system of decentralized energy generation from renewables. As a group, RWE, E.on, Vattenfall and EnBW account for only five per cent of the installed capacity of renewables, whereas the share of households and farmers is 46 per cent. According to a survey by LAB & Company, a head-hunting firm, three quarters of the managers at the German energy giants admit that their firms missed the Energiewende train and that their current business models cannot survive.

No wonder they fight against a fundamental change of the system, and as hard and long as they can.

The battle of the systems since Fukushima (I): from "electricity gap" to putting a brake on renewables

By October 28, 2010, the big utilities had successfully convinced the federal CDU/CSU/FDP government to modify an earlier decision of the red-green Schröder government; in 2000 the cabinet of Ms Merkel's predecessor had decided to phase out nuclear power. Now the permitted life spans of seven older nuclear power plants were extended by eight years, the other ten got 14 years more. But after Fukushima, it was clear that this phase-out of the phase-out of nuclear power had lost all political support.

What now?

After eight of the nuclear reactors had been shut down, the opponents of renewables began selling the story of the "electricity gap" up and down the country. The message: "For heaven's sake, renewables cannot replace nuclear power so quickly." We will be sitting in the cold and dark, the economy will collapse, and nothing else will work either. As it turned out, no one had to sit in the cold and dark.

On the contrary. During the very cold month of February 2012, we exported electricity to France when that country's nuclear reactors were operating at the limit. Germany has also been exporting electricity in 2013: we produce more than we need at home. The electricity gap never materialized. So they had to come up with yet another argument: "We have too much renewable electricity."

Too much?

Only a short while ago, they had claimed that before 2022 renewables could not possibly take over from the nuclear power stations that had been shut down. They then proposed to put a lid on the share of renewables in total electricity production: no more than 35 per cent by 2022. The reason is no longer that it cannot happen, but that it is happening too fast.

The new grand coalition government, led by Ms Merkel, has taken up this idea in its "Eckpunktepapier". As mentioned before, this "corner stone" policy paper was presented by Sigmar Gabriel who is not only vice chancellor but also in charge of a super ministry, the combination of two previous ministries: economy and energy. The main aim is to control the speed of the Energiewende by introducing annual limits to the expansion of electricity from renewables and to grant the producers of conventional power a longer transition period. They can look forward to a further recovery of their profits—these had been hit by the shut-down of the nuclear plants. That it will now take longer to reduce emissions of carbon dioxide than seemed possible only a short while ago is obviously acceptable to the black & red coalition partners. The environment takes a back seat.

The opponents of the Energiewende are presently relying on one key argument: green electricity will become more and more expensive—which means the poor are suffering most.

Peter Altmaier, who was in charge of the environment portfolio toward the end of the second Merkel government, also used this argument when I talked to him shortly before he was going to implement, with a lot of publicity, the so-called electricity price brake. It was in spring 2013. The next federal elections were scheduled for September 22 of that year. If the Energiewende became too expensive, it would lose its appeal—and that had to be avoided. Unless the system of feed-in tariffs was changed, ie, the EEG law, the overall costs would rise to 1,000 billion euros. Many people were impressed by this number and have since become convinced that the Energiewende is too expensive—and a major risk.

According to Altmaier, it was nice and worthwhile to reduce damages to the environment, but for someone living on a pension or for a father of a family this is "only a small comfort if they don't know how to pay their electricity bills". He also brought up my favorite—the problem that the wind does not blow 24 hours a day. "We need additional conventional power plants as a reserve—for the time when the sun does not shine and the wind does not blow".

To get me right: I met Mr. Altmaier on several occasions; he is a pleasant person and a competent politician, but at the time he was mainly a populist on the campaign trail. He was also held back by his FDP cabinet colleague Philipp Rösler, the minister of the economy. In another government, such as the new one, he could have been exactly the right person to promote the Energiewende. As it happened, the environment portfolio in the grand coalition went to the SPD, while Altmaier has become the minister of the chancellery. In the longer run, it may actually turn out to be an advantage for the promoters of the Energiewende that he now works with Angela Merkel on a daily basis. We will find out.

The battle of the systems since Fukushima (II): blame the EEG-levy

It is correct that electricity must be affordable. It is not correct that the EEG-levy alone is held responsible for rapidly rising electricity prices.

The EEG law is the basis of the Energiewende. Since 2000, it provides long-term guarantees of feed-in tariffs and priority grid access for electricity from renewables. This means that everyone who produces renewable electricity can pump it into the electricity grid at a fixed price.

The 2013 EEG-levy was 5.28 cents per kilowatt-hour. It rose to 6.24 cents in 2014. For an average household which consumes 4,000 kilowatt-hours per year, that means 20.8 euros a month.

But electricity prices are rising for other reasons as well, reasons that have nothing to do with the EEG-levy. The large utilities use the levy as an alibi for price rigging. According to a study of the Universität für Technik und Forschung des Saarlandes (Saarland University of Technology and Research), the utilities had quadrupled their profits between 2002 and 2009. Unimpressed, they and their protégés continue to use their favorite mantra: renewables drive up the price of electricity, burning coal makes it affordable. What use is a clean environment if we can no longer pay for electricity?

The EEG law does exactly what it is supposed to do—provide incentives for the production of electricity from renewables, for technological progress and lower prices. It is, in line with Hermann Scheer's ideas, the first systemic structural change of the energy sector—it codifies the priority of renewables. That is why it is effective. And that's why vested interests are fighting it.

Without the new institutional framework, the transformation from dirty to clean energy would have stalled half-way. Several decades ago, the state had promoted nuclear energy—without its enormous financial support, the industry would not have expanded the way it did. According to a Greenpeace-sponsored study of the "Forum Ökologisch-Soziale Marktwirtschaft" (Forum Environmental and Social Market Economy), government subsidies for nuclear power amounted to 164.7 billion euros in the period 1950 to 2008. The coal industry has also been heavily subsidized.

Power from renewables is different because the state does not contribute to the cost of start-ups: the buyers of electricity indirectly pay for that. What is more, they also bear the cost of large energy companies which are partly or fully exempt from the EEG-levy; in 2012 this indirect subsidy was about 2.5 billion euros. Today, it is definitely much higher: in 2012, about 730 firms received exemptions and discounts; in 2014 their number had climbed to no less than 2,098. The "Bund der Energieverbraucher" (Association of Energy Consumers) estimates that the increase of the EEG-levy in recent years is, to a large degree, due to the "unlawful exemption of large companies by the federal government". They are subsidized by the other consumers of electricity. I wonder why, for instance, a nurse—who usually has a low salary—should financially support business firms, many of them rich and in good health. Is that really fair and ethical? And these are actually not the only costs born by us, the consumers.

Currently, society must also shoulder the huge follow-on costs of coal and nuclear policies. A study by Greenpeace Energy puts the total amount of subsidies that went to coal and nuclear power stations at 429 billion euros (since 1970). The "hidden fee that consumers pay for conventional power", including social costs, is estimated to be 10.2 cents per kilowatt-hour. The public pays for this in ways that are not obvious. The electricity bill reflects only some of the social costs caused by the producers of conventional energy. If all these subsidies, the damages caused by the production and burning of coal, the costs for the disposal of nuclear waste and other related (external) costs would be included in the price of conventional electricity, it would become clear that it is anything but cheap—not to mention the potentially extremely high costs of a reactor blow-up.

At the same time, the increasing supply of electricity from renewables continues to reduce its price at the energy exchange in Leipzig. In 2013, the average price of one kilowatt hour for "immediate delivery" was just 3.78 euro cents! In previous years prices used to be higher, but never more than 6.57 cents (2008). The trend is down.

Big industry and the energy establishment couldn't be happier, but households do not benefit at all—the low costs are not passed on to them. They pay the full EEG-levy. The system massively benefits the profits of the large utilities. These are complaining about the high costs of closing down several nuclear power plants in 2011 and 2012, but they continue to earn healthy profits.

Bottom line: the EEG law is used to redistribute income from private households to the large utilities. It makes me mad when I hear politicians like Brüderle saying that the EEG-levy is the only reason electricity prices are rising. Note that the government also gets additional revenue from the 19% value-added tax: the higher the price of electricity the happier the tax authorities! The losers include pensioners, the group of people someone like Altmaier is supposedly so concerned about. To quote from a Wirtschaftswoche interview with Jürgen Trittin, former chair of the Greens in the Berlin parliament as well as a former minister for the environment, "We do not have a cost problem, but rather a problem with a government that tries to slow the expansion of green energy; it wants to make sure that coal-burning power plants do not lose money".

The horror scenarios about millions of people whithout electricity serve not only the purpose of making the EEG law the main scapegoat for higher electricity prices but also to avoid having to discuss other issues, for instance rising gasoline prices or how to reduce our dependence on (mostly imported) oil and gas.

I do not want to shrug off the problem that the poor have a hard time paying their electricity bills. I once stood in the post office next to someone whose electricity had been turned off by the provider. To turn it on again, he had to pay his debt. He had brought all the coins he could find and put them on the counter, one by one—it was visibly difficult for him. The scene is still vividly in my mind today.

Most people are not familiar with the details of their electricity bills—and are neither aware of the actual costs nor the savings potential. If they were on the brink of financial ruin, it would be different. If politicians were really so concerned about the poor and their ability to buy electricity—as they should –, they could easily design a system that takes account of social problems. I prefer the idea of progressive tariffs, comparable to the income tax system: those who consume little pay little; today it's the other way around. The tariffs could be calculated on a per-person or a multi-member family basis. The first kilowatt-hours are less expensive than the following ones. This raises the awareness of how much it costs to waste electricity and thus creates an incentive to economize. Overall, less money would be spent on electricity, and a considerably larger sum of money could be saved this way than by slowing down the growth rate of energy production from renewables.

Even so, it is not a question for me that the EEG must continuously be reformed. New situations arise as renewables take an ever larger share in electricity generation. Something that was mandatory at an early stage of the process is no longer mandatory at an advanced stage.

Up to now, wind and sun were the variable elements while nuclear power and coal provided the base load.

We are now at a point where the two worlds must be brought together.

But the essentials will remain the same at each stage and must be retained, especially the broad participation of small investors and ordinary people in general. We need incentives as well as a limitation of financial risks. Since renewables do not cost anything at the margin, the electricity price is determined almost exclusively by amortization—which depends on interest rates and the expected economic life of the facilities. A system of feed-in prices that are fixed for a long period is therefore the best model. Only in this way is it possible to maximize the write-down period and minimize the debt service—which increases investors' financial returns. Market risks would be considerably higher without guaranteed feed-in prices. These risks would reduce investments in renewable energy and lead to higher prices for consumers.

When a fixed amount of electricity is being tendered, ie, fully exposed to the interaction of demand and supply—as the FDP has demanded again and again—small operators lose the basis for long-term planning. For economic reasons, smaller companies and normal people would be excluded from those tenders.

And that's supposed to be liberal? That's supposed to be a standard feature of a market economy? For me, that is a planned economy for the benefit of the large utilities.

The battle of the systems after Fukushima (III): the attempt to re-establish old structures

After successfully slowing down photovoltaics (PV), "old energy" has resumed its battle against wind mills again, more specifically against onshore wind.

Here we are in the advanced stage of the battle of the systems. It is no longer just about renewables against fossil energies, but also about renewables against renewables.

Why?

Offshore electricity generation seems, at first sight, the solution to almost all problems. The wind wheels are located far away from the shore in the ocean. It is possible to generate lots of electricity. The wind is always strong there. The previous conservative-liberal (CDU/CSU/FDP) government of Angela Merkel regarded offshore as an important element of the Energiewende, just as the conservative-social democrat (CDU/CSU/SPD) and social democrat-green (SPD/Green) governments before her. By 2020, 1,500 to 2,500 offshore wind mills are supposed to generate an output of 10,000 megawatts, the equivalent of four to five nuclear reactors. The goal for 2030 is 25,000 megawatts.

But by June 2013, only 116 offshore wind wheels with a total capacity of 520 megawatts were generating electricity. By August 2013, permissions existed for 30 wind parks in the North Sea and 3 in the Baltic Sea, a total of 2,250 turbines.

For comparison, in 2013 the 23,600 onshore wind mills had an installed capacity of 33,700 megawatt.

When someone in Frankfurt, Stuttgart or Munich buys one kilowatt-hour of electricity generated in the North Sea, he or she usually assumes that this is relatively inexpensive: on the ocean there is more wind than on land. But how will the electricity be transported to the south? A long, expensive and currently not even existing transport corridor would have to be built. In calm weather, there would be no electricity, and when the wind blows it would not be possible to store the energy—or only at high costs. That cannot be successful—not only because 4,500 kilometers of high-voltage power lines are missing.

I know that there are advocates of the Energiewende who are convinced that we need both: onshore and offshore.

I see it differently: this kind of electricity generation is of course renewable and clean, but it is centralized (in terms of ownership and geography), it requires long and expensive high voltage power lines, it is far from consumers, difficult to manage and therefore anything but optimal. Above all, it is a business model for the large utilities, just as operating the grid and the storage facilities. Offshore sites are unaffordable for cooperatives or local communities, and usually even for networks of local utilities. To put it as it is: offshore wind power is an expensive subsidy of "old energy", without the participation of normal citizens. It is a continuation of the old energy system. In an analysis for the Verbraucherzentrale Bundesverband (Federal Association of Consumers), consumer watchdog Holger Krawinkel argues that "internationally, sea wind will only make sense in shallow water near the coast; in Germany this area is a nature preserve and can thus not be used for wind parks". He suggests that the faster these offshore projects are given up, the lower the cost to society.

But how about the many new jobs that Erwin Sellering, state premier of Mecklenburg-Vorpommern, is betting on? It is understandable that he focuses on the labor market of his relatively poor state, but his view is nevertheless shortsighted.

Initially, building offshore wind parks will create only approximately 18,000 new jobs in all of Germany (2012). What should be taken into account, though, is that even in Mecklenburg-Vorpommern many more jobs could be generated by onshore wind parks—these cost only about 30 per cent of offshore parks. The reason: in the future, many energy intensive companies will go to windy places where they can become self-sufficient by installing short and therefore inexpensive direct lines to the nearest wind park.

Supporters of the Energiewende often say that we have to offer the big 4 utilities the perspective of an offshore alternative, otherwise they would try to hang on to their fossil and nuclear power plants as long as they can. What perspectives has Baden-Württemberg's state-owned nuclear power producer EnBW after the end of the nuclear age? Why not let them run a few wind parks on the coast? That sounds plausible at first sight, but it is not. We are in the middle of a battle of the systems where only one will survive. The next nuclear power plant shut-down is scheduled for 2015. Afterwards, the large utilities will use all the tricks they know and the power they have to keep the remaining power stations, just as they are instrumentalizing the issue of those supposedly indispensable new electricity corridors across the country.

According to the grid development plan of 2012, around 2,800 kilometers of new electricity corridors are to be built, from north to south. Sounds plausible because most nuclear power plants are in southern Germany while the Länder (states) with lots of wind are on the coast in the north.

Meteorologists tell us that calm days in the north often mean windy or even stormy days in the south and southwest. In other words, if we build new wind parks there, we increase the country's electric capacity and stabilize the grids.

Inland parks in the south have another advantage: steady winds. This means less has to be spent on new grids and storage facilities which even out the daily and seasonal peaks and troughs of electricity demand. In northern Germany the average wind speed is higher, but the variation around that average is considerable—poison for the grids. The idea of "wind energy only in the north" is therefore wrong. A well-balanced distribution of wind energy across the country is the solution: it minimizes system costs.

By the way, modern light-wind generators can already reach full capacity at moderate wind speeds. At locations with an average speed of only 6.25 m/s, more than 4,000 hours a year at full load are possible.

But things are not so easy: the German electricity grids are a powerful trump card. This is often not fully appreciated. By owning the grids, the 4 big utilities have for many years been able to keep their considerable political influence. In their pursuit of high profits they have not taken good care of the grid—which is why it is partially outdated and prone to failures.

Against its original intention, the EU commission has not succeeded to separate the production and distribution of electricity. RWE simply founded a subsidiary, Amprion, for its grids; Vattenfall has 50 Hertz. Only E.on, the largest of the four utilities, has actually sold its grids—to Tennet, a Dutch 100% state-owned grid operator. In the meantime, Germany's Federal Network Agency is to plan and coordinate the expansion of the grids.

But the big players have their own plans. According to a study by "BUND", a large organization of nature conservationists, Germany's branch of Friends of the Earth, the utilities are planning oversized new grids—financed by the public, as readers may not be surprised to learn—to transport electricity from coal plants in the north to consumers in the south. By 2022, coal power plants are scheduled to generate almost 250 terawatt-hours, up to 100 terawatt-hours more than in the scenarios of the previous German government. This alone translates into additional annual emissions of about 90 million tons of CO_2 by 2022.

Why is the energy establishment keen on the massive expansion of the national grid? Because it would make the feed-in priority of renewables less of a challenge for them. If the capacity of the grid increases a lot, electricity from brown coal can also flow unhampered, anytime. The coal plants do not have to be scaled down or shut down when there is enough electricity from renewables. Instead, they can continue to produce electricity at full blast and sell it abroad. From a business point of view such a strategy makes sense for the large utilities, but if they get their way, one can forget about electricity production with little or no carbon dioxide emissions. We are talking here about an indirect promotion of new coal power plants.

It would be a major setback for the environment. Lorenz Jarass, an economics professor from Wiesbaden, grid expert and government consultant, acknowledges the need to reinforce existing power lines. But the grids should not be designed to accommodate peak loads. An aggressive expansion of the grid is bad for the Energiewende because it would help to increase the grid input of conventional power plants. The government's climate policies would be reduced to absurdity.

And all this is at the expense of the people. The BUND NGO fears that the current grid plans would not only allow higher rates of capacity utilization at the coal power plants but may also make it easier to build new ones. The grid operators' forecasts that the brown coal power plants would run 8,000 hours a year at full load by 2022 (a year has 8,760 hours) is not only considerably above current averages but also above the technical possibilities of existing plants.

Coal power plants are supposedly needed for another reason—the lack of storage facilities for the electricity generated by wind and sun. As long as that problem has not been solved, we will have to rely on coal-burning power plants.

First of all, the closer to the consumer the production of electricity, the less storage is needed. And second, technological progress depends on demand and thus on the existence of a market, as well as on government support—the early-stage costs are considerable. In general, the technologies for storage, production and distribution of renewable energies will be ready when they are needed. If coal-burning power plants are now being built to cover the base load, there is no incentive to push ahead with innovative storage technologies. It would be counterproductive—no market demand for advanced storage facilities, no progress on that front.

Many arguments against the Energiewende depend on a key point: the supply of electricity from renewables fluctuates a lot. During calm periods wind turbines do not feed electricity into the grid, but when there is a storm, with wind speeds of more than 13 meters per second, they run at full capacity. Gas-powered stations can flexibly fill the gaps, but coal burning plants cannot. It does not make sense to rely on them for base load purposes. Once the share of renewables in total electricity output exceeds 35 per cent, the coal power plants must be turned off so often that they stop earning money for the operators.

While this is good news for the supporters of the Energiewende, it is bad news for the large utilities. For them and their lobbyists, the priority is to keep the coal-burning power plants running for as long as possible—before it is too late. Not too late for the climate or the future of society, but for their profits.

Once a new coal power plant has started to run, it runs. For many decades it produces money for the owners and climate-damaging emissions for the planet. We are at a point where our energy and climate policies will be decided for the next 40 years. Old coal-burning power plants must be switched off for good in the coming decade. But then what—new coal-burning power plants? Or decentralized electricity from renewables?

The new system of people's energy

To summarize: we are faced with a classic conflict of interests. The old system defends its interests against the new system. The established energy providers try to hold off the energy revolution. Because they live well in the old system. The faster and the more comprehensive the Energiewende, the faster revenues from selling electricity will flow elsewhere. They know that there is no place for the large utilities in a world of decentralized energy production.

That is essential, for it will be the end of the status quo.

Today, regions where power plants are located or which are importers of electricity do not participate in the revenues from energy production. But their natural environment is often destroyed, and their resources depleted, such as by strip mining 31 square kilometers at Garzweiler (near Mönchengladbach and Neuss). Some are left with nuclear waste, as at the "famous" disposal site of Gorleben in Lower Saxony. All of them have to cope with emissions of poisonous dirt—which in turn is mainly responsible for global climate change. Dirty energy only looks cheap, but actually is not: many external costs such as the damage to the environment and health hazards are not included in the price paid by the consumers of electricity.

The public has to pay the bill in the form of higher taxes and health insurance premiums.
The new system is characterized by lots of small decentralized power stations. The owners are regional players such as communities, energy cooperatives, private households and farmers. Their priorities are value creation at a local and individual level, and the protection of the environment: there are no harmful emissions. Not all revenues remain in the region or community, but more often than not they do.
According to a study by the "trend:research" institute in Bremen, households own 46 per cent of Germany's renewable energy facilities. They are the largest players in what is developing into our society's most important market. By now, renewable energy producers have lobby organizations as well—they try to change the policy process in their favor. These lobbies are still small compared to the enormous networks of the old-style energy providers.
Indeed, I don't think the new energy players have an effective lobby yet. They urgently need one.
They should be represented in all political parties, from left to right. While the established energy firms are closely involved in all political processes, the members of the new system are standing on the sidelines. They may organize demonstrations but do not really take part in the battle and are therefore unable to have their voices heard where it matters most. That is not ok. It is unfair if only one boxer is allowed in the ring. Decentralized energy is crucial for our future. The representatives of "new energy" must play a more important, even a decisive role in shaping the policies of the Energiewende. They must participate more actively.
We have to fight for our goals.

9

A vision for the future

How a free, independent and good life could look like in 2033

If you do not know where you want to go, you cannot find the right path. Similarly, in the current political situation, reforming the EEG law (Renewable Energy Law) first requires an idea about the future structure of energy supply. What does society want, and how will it produce and live? Not before this is clear can we seriously discuss the various ways to get there. First the goal, then the decision about the best road. At the moment, politicians believe they can simultaneously keep the old system and somehow create a new one. Large utilities and people power. Coal and renewables. Centralized and decentralized. To have one's cake and eat it, too.
It will not work.

An excursion into the future

March 3, 2033 in Munich. Germany's national soccer team plays Italy. Germany wins 2:0, after goals in minutes 83 and 89.
I watch the game with my friend Luca. Ten minutes before the end I use my smart watch to order an Autro.
Five minutes after the final whistle it pulls up in front of the arena.
There is enough space because the traffic situation is completely different from the one twenty years ago. There are hardly any parking lots. The entire space is filled with moving vehicles—buses, trams and arriving and departing Autros.
Luca and I sit down behind each other in the driverless, two-person Autro, which purrs off right away. We talk about how strange it was when we had our own cars. Absurd. While the Autro darts along the Autrobahn, we watch a summary of the game on the monitors and are back home in Mainz 90 minutes later—430 kilometers from the stadium.

The trip is so short because most of the time we are on a high-speed route where the Autro moves on rails, like a super train. There are never any traffic jams on the Autrobahn. Compared to the "good old days", mobility is thus dramatically better. The Autro runs 100 per cent on renewables. Some of the electricity is generated by the car's paint—which captures the energy of the sun during the day. Twenty minutes before our arrival, sitting in the Autro, I use my smart watch again, this time to turn on the heat of my house, close the shutters and illuminate the southern wall in black, red and gold, the national colors. This is not nationalism but something a soccer fan likes to do. The games between the leading European soccer nations are among the last remaining opportunities to assert national identities—we are living in the United States of Europe; political and economic differences are not large anymore.

Organic solar cells on the house

For a long time already, my house has been a self-sufficient "active energy house" and is not connected to the electricity grid anymore. It not only consumes but also produces energy—the exception are the few pellets I need for the fireplace. The same thing, incidentally, at the football stadium: its outer shell is completely covered with organic solar cells made of hydrocarbon compounds; these are inexpensive, easy to handle and, in the meantime, very efficient. During the day, the solar cells produce and store electricity.

All nuclear power plants have been shut down; even the French ones. They had become too expensive. And the Chinese had to turn off their last coal burning power plant three years ago, in 2030—the air had become so bad that there was no other way.

The new thinking is most evident in business. Energy-intensive firms have left their old locations and are now in places with lots of wind and sun. In terms of cost they believed they had no other choice. Several well-known companies have moved their headquarters from the south to the northern states of Schleswig-Holstein and Mecklenburg-Vorpommern. This had caused a political uproar. Even though sun and wind conditions are excellent near the ocean, these moves had not been absolutely necessary. There are plenty of good locations in southern Germany as well, in regions which are also flourishing by now. These locations are often on the ridges of low mountain ranges or in the Black Forest. They not only get plenty of sun but also strong winds.

Photovoltaics has long been a standard feature of average households. It is used almost everywhere. Wherever possible, the outside of buildings is covered by solar cells. Alternatively, houses are coated with a special paint which produces electricity. Today's solar cells have an efficiency factor of 50 per cent. The modules are flexible: electricity which is produced around lunchtime but is not needed immediately is routinely stored in batteries in the basement or in the Autros. Today's batteries are no longer large and heavy, but super thin and integrated into the car body.

The electricity can also be transformed into gas which can then be fed into gas pipelines. From there it may end up in micro CHP units. In addition, I also use my body to produce energy: high-performance modules are integrated into my clothing. This allows me to recharge my mobile devices directly and very conveniently.

The advanced modules can capture the entire spectrum of light, not just parts of it as twenty years ago. As long as there is light outside, early in the morning or late in the day, there is solar radiation which we can transform into electricity.

In the few cases when solar electricity is not sufficient for my needs, some of the heat from the pellet burner is used to generate electricity, covering the shortfall. The pellets are automatically delivered once a year. They are burned efficiently and leave no ash. In winter, when it is bitingly cold outside, the pellet burner just runs a little more than usual.

Extremely low energy costs

Apart from that, all my devices are programmed to consume energy at a time when the photovoltaic facilities are producing energy, especially at midday. I have reduced energy costs dramatically by combining electricity and heat generation and by using energy-efficient household and technical devices. LED is the source of light in 2033—it comes in various colors, including very warm ones.

My TV is no longer huge, bulky and a big consumer of electricity. It is manufactured without much energy, and runs very economically. My living room wall has a special paint coat which doubles as a screen. I can vary the size of the picture as I like, even up to cinema format. Electricity consumption will nevertheless be moderate—comparable to what I needed for standby twenty years ago.

Sometimes you want to watch television not on your smart watch or with your smart glasses, but prefer the full sound and a large cinema-like screen. Like now, for example. My friend Luca has come in for a beer. As an expert of football tactics, he is still occupied with the game in Munich. He uses his smart glasses to analyze the mistakes of the Italian defense during the final ten minutes. He takes his beer from a refrigerator which uses its waste heat to generate electricity. By the way, they still exist—the good, old cars with combustion engines. But only very few. Only the superrich have such cars; normal people cannot afford gasoline anymore. These cars are just driven for nostalgic reasons. No one regards a car as a symbol of freedom and independence anymore. For me, economic freedom and independence means being able to produce and consume my own energy.

In 2033, people are independent in ways no one could have imagined two decades ago.

That is what motivates me: a future where everybody has an easy, independent and cheap access to energy.

It is for this reason that I am making my indecent proposal to the German chancellor. It is for this reason that I would be very happy if she accepted my offer. Renewables give us the chance to strengthen our democracy and live a full and self-determined life. This is the basis for progress, just as for global peace and cooperation.

If we want this future, we have to lay the rails now.

The master plan

How we can successfully accomplish the Energiewende in a very short time

Introduction: the idea behind the master plan

The thing about the future is that no one can say for sure what will happen. You can, however, try to shape it to some extent. I find this more useful and exciting than just hoping that things will turn out well. That is why I'm writing this book: to explain in a non-technical way how our energy future based 100 per cent on renewables could look like, and how it would work. The policy alternatives need to be understood before making decisions about renewables. It is easy to distinguish between people who are for progress and those who are trying to slow it—those who want to shape the future have clear goals, the others look for reasons why things won't work or why it will take longer than expected.

My aim is to clarify today which energy system is the best and cheapest in the long run. That is why I have developed a master plan. I am inviting readers to make critical comments—constructive ones, I hope.

The assumptions at the heart of this plan reflect what I know. To be sure, this is not a scientific research paper but rather a practitioner's blueprint of the best way to achieve the goal of 100 per cent energy from renewables. I am not specific about power levels, tariffs, the optimal location of wind mills or storage systems. Instead, I try to make readers understand an extremely complex process; it is actually getting more complex the closer you look at the details. It's not about being right about everything. It's about formulating what we want to achieve in the future. What should we do today to get there?

To start, I have to answer some fundamental questions: will the world population continue to grow? Will we require even more energy?

And last but not least, what does it mean for the price of energy that the world is gradually running out of fossil fuels?

Why do we need the master plan?
Because soon energy from fossil fuels will not be affordable anymore.

The price of crude oil has increased from about 25 dollars at the beginning of the last decade to 106 dollars in the spring of 2014. That is a fact. The world's energy consumption will probably double over the next twenty years. Peak oil, the point at which the maximum rate of petroleum extraction is reached, is getting closer. The daily amount of oil, coal and gas that we burn took nature a million years to produce. We have already used up a large portion of the earth's resources, and in doing so have polluted the atmosphere and upset the climate. Our present lifestyle is not sustainable.

Cost of energy: 1992, 2002 and 2012

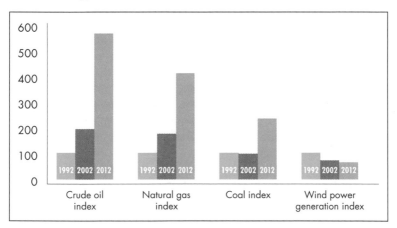

Sources: German Federal Ministry of the Economy and Technology, 2013; Deutsche Windguard, 2013

It's possible that fracking will allow the US to reduce its dependence on imported gas and oil for a few years, but the relief won't last for more than one generation. The US is no longer the world's largest consumer of energy anyway. China is number one now. Other

large emerging nations such as India and Brazil continue to indus-
trialize rapidly. Their rising living standards will inevitably boost
energy consumption.

The 82 million Germans are driving approximately 50 million cars.
On a global scale, there are over 800 million cars and the world
population now exceeds 7 billion; it will soon reach 9 billion. Can
we forbid the rising middle classes to consume the way we do?
Surely not. So let's assume that almost every adult will own a car, a
cell phone, a laptop, a refrigerator, a TV and an air conditioner.

This means that energy consumption in the next fifteen to twenty
years will not only increase by 50 per cent, but by much more, certainly by more than we are presently expecting.

It is absolutely impossible to rely on cheap oil to meet all our future
energy needs. Most importantly, our planet cannot accommodate
billions of additional cars and air conditioners powered by fossil
fuels: the world's temperature would continue to rise dangerously.
Trying to extend the fossil fuel age doesn't just affect polar bears
and other animals, it will lead to food crises, weather catastrophes,
as well as large-scale migration, even wars caused by climate
change. Not to forget, oil is the "lubricant" of the economy: it is not
just needed to generate energy but for many other purposes as well,
for instance for the production of plastics and pharmaceuticals. We
can no longer afford to simply burn it and to destroy the atmosphere in the process.

So here we are: shrinking resources, rising demand and supply of
energy-intensive goods and services, an accelerating deterioration
of the environment. On the other hand, a depletion of the world's
reserves of fossil fuels. Every liter of oil that is burned is lost forever.
You don't need to have an MBA to know that supply and demand
determine prices. The less there is of a product and the stronger the
demand for it, the more expensive it gets. The Energiewende is not
only about social and ecological issues, it also has a big impact on
the economy. The euro crisis can to some extent be interpreted as an
energy crisis—the countries in the so-called periphery came close
to defaulting partly because of their steeply rising bills for energy
imports. The truth is that Europe pays much more for electricity and
gasoline than it can afford.

The basic thesis of this master plan is therefore: because fossil
fuels are getting so expensive, conventional energy will no longer
be affordable.

If we continue to burn ever larger amounts of fossil fuels, there will inevitably be revolutions and wars over those finite and increasingly expensive resources. At the same time, the quality of our environment will get worse and worse. Another effect is probably the concentration of economic power: governments can be held hostage by a few global companies and cartels. Civil liberties may well fall by the wayside. Sites will be cleared, towns and neighborhoods will give way for huge excavators that extract the last drop of oil from slate and tar sands, requiring ever more energy and releasing even more of those dangerous greenhouse gases. This kind of production is very expensive, but as oil and gas prices keep rising it will be profitable for a while. Even our most beautiful natural landscapes will no longer be off limits. The same goes for fracking, a method for extracting natural gas from deep down. It uses poisonous chemicals which pollute our drinking water. Fracking is not a feasible solution, despite claims to the contrary. It is a continuation of old energy policies and simply postpones the day of reckoning.

What will happen to energy prices in Germany?

The decisive factor is the price of fossil fuels: will it remain stable? Presently Germany has to pay about 120 billion euros annually for oil, gas and coal. To put this number into perspective: the country's GDP will be about 2,840bn euros in 2014.

In spring 2013, I had the opportunity to visit Peter Altmaier at his office in Berlin; he was federal environment minister at the time. Shortly before he had presented a paper about the "Strompreisbremse"—a plan to put a "brake on electricity prices". Using pen and paper, he showed me how he arrived at one trillion euros—the estimated total cost of the Energiewende. A large share of that scary number reflected the cost of renovating the housing stock. Of course, existing buildings are responsible for approximately one third of our CO_2 emissions—but this has nothing to do with the EEG-levy that is a component of people's electricity bills. Nevertheless, his mathematics were correct on a lot of points.

But the calculation was based on the assumption that the prices for renewables will remain the same. He ignored recent innovations and learning curves—and the price reductions that have already occurred as a result. More importantly, Altmaier made the assumption that the prices of fossil fuels will fall, if only slightly. In my opinion, this is a serious mistake.

Energiewende sichern – Kosten begrenzen

Minister Altmaier recognizing the work I've done to promote the Energiewende.

If you look at global population, production and consumption trends, it is clear that German prices of fossil fuels will inevitably rise in the medium term. Within two decades, an annual increase of just a few per cent will drive up the cost of importing fossil fuels from currently 100 billion euros a year to perhaps 250 billion. For comparison: in 2013 the federal government's total outlays were approximately 340 billion euros. Even if you assume that the cost of oil will only double in the next 20 years, the average household's heating oil bill would jump from 2,000 to 4,000 euros. If the price were to quadruple, many Germans would no longer be able to own cars or heat their homes.

The focus of the public debate is presently on the annual 15 or 20 billion euros that households are charged to support the Energiewende. This is equivalent to 0.6 per cent of GDP and thus a small price to pay for energy independence and a cleaner environment. If politicians would set honest prices for CO_2 emissions, the certificates would trade between 30 and 70 euros per metric ton. According to some educated guesses there is presently a surplus of about 1.8 billion certificates in the European Union—this is why they persistently cost less than 5 euros. There is de facto no incentive for business to invest in low-emission technology. A side effect of the low price of the certificates is that the utilities find it profitable to burn more coal. More recently, the shale gas revolution in the US has led to a reduction of coal demand there, followed by rising US coal exports which in turn have depressed coal prices in world markets. Coal is so cheap that it has become considerably less attractive to operate the much cleaner gas fired power stations. For the environment these developments are a catastrophe.

In 2012, no less than 317 million tons of CO_2 were blown into the German atmosphere. If polluters had to pay 30 euros per ton, that would generate about 10 billion euros per year for the state. I mention these numbers to give readers an idea of the order of magnitude we are talking about.

The cost of nuclear power cannot be accurately calculated or forecast: taxpayers will have to bear most of the cost for the disposal of nuclear waste and for decommissioning the nuclear power plants. A worst-case accident such as Fukushima would be extremely costly for society. Taxpayers have already paid billions of euros for nuclear energy and billions more are needed in the future. We cannot entirely eliminate these decommissioning costs, even if we immediately switch to 100 per cent energy from renewables. What we can do, though, is to limit the risks and costs. A nuclear catastrophe must be prevented by all means.

At the same time, we are currently paying a lot for imported fossil fuels and uranium—too much of the value created by German business has to be sent abroad to pay for that. We subsidize the energy consumption of business, but the external cost of ruining the environment must in the end be shouldered by society. This has to change.

What are the consequences of burning fossil fuels to produce electricity? Resources are shrinking and will become very expensive, there will be conflicts down the road over those resources, and the global climate is being destroyed at a rate that threatens the future of our children.

Is the road into the abyss "without an alternative", as we often hear from politicians, or is there a solution that eliminates these costs? Much of the supply of fossil fuels comes from unstable regions such as Russia or the Middle East; their prices will most likely increase over the medium term. How can we keep our economy competitive while reducing our dependence on the large utilities?

Is there an alternative?

The alternative: wind and solar power

The logical way out of the dilemma I just described is simple: we have to stop using coal, oil, gas and uranium to generate our energy— we have to become independent of these resources.

To base a country's energy supply on the assumption that commodity prices will remain stable is highly speculative and thus incredibly risky. If we rely just on sun and wind, we do not need imported fossil fuels, we'd stop to destroy the atmosphere, avoid the dangerous speculation about the price of fossil fuels and benefit from reliably stable prices. That is a fundamental difference.

How do we get from here to there? By betting on a combination of wind and sun, on the two resources which are de facto both unlimited and cheap. It's the perfect solution for Germany. Hydroelectricity works well in countries like Norway, Switzerland or Costa Rica. In Germany, this source of energy will only play a fairly minor—but not insignificant—role. Geothermal electricity is potentially also available in huge quantities but fairly expensive so far. Overall, renewables can cover all our energy needs. And they are available for free once the infrastructure has been put in place. Every day the sun sends 15,000 times more energy to the earth than we currently consume. The power of wind and sun can be harvested anywhere. It does not have a market price. The price for energy from renewables is almost entirely defined by the amount of the initial investment.

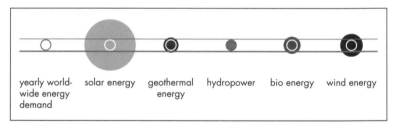

yearly world-wide energy demand   solar energy   geothermal energy   hydropower   bio energy   wind energy

The sun provides many times more energy than we need globally.

The graph is a stylized description of the relationship between the world's annual consumption of energy—the empty circle on the left—and the various sources of renewable energy than can be used to meet this demand. Message number one: there is no need for fossil fuel or uranium. Message number two: solar power is by far the largest potential source of energy, followed by wind. Message number three: a smart mix of renewables can generate all the energy the world needs, free of charge and forever.

Technical progress is almost unstoppable. I have no doubt that innovations will continue to make renewables even cheaper over time. But we have to start now in order to avoid rising bills for fossil fuels and the external costs of ruining the environment. The prices of renewable energy include all such costs. There are no hidden costs because wind and solar energy don't create any. They don't have a negative impact on the environment, there is no such thing as nuclear waste and they don't heat up the world's atmosphere.

We will no longer depend on imports from unstable countries. The Ukrainian crisis has once again shown the risks of such an exposure. We will no longer rely on the large utilities whose priority is the maximization of profits, no matter what this means for the rest of the population. What's most important to me, the master plan is not an unrealistic plan to save the world. Its aim is to combine wind and solar power in a way that guarantees a reliable source of energy—at unbeatably low prices. Renewables are therefore not only the solution from an ecological and social, but also from an economic perspective.

Why wind and solar power? The general framework of the master plan

The master plan addresses the following specific issues: What are the best locations for the production of electricity from renewables? Should all wind mills be in northern Germany and all photovoltaic systems in the south? What is the role of hydroelectricity and biomass? They have the advantage that they can generate a steady supply of electricity. How much storage capacity do we need, and is it actually possible to create such storage facilities?

For an optimal energy supply system, some basics have to be considered. For me, this includes storage facilities, transportation, weather, availability of renewable power, and the role of hydroelectricity and bioenergy.

Storage

Several different technologies are available for the storage of electricity. But this is and will continue to be the most expensive way to use electricity. For various reasons, energy that is drawn from a storage facility is two to three times more expensive than energy that is consumed directly. Capital expenditures for constructing storage facilities are almost as high as those for power plants. Since storage systems are only used infrequently, the number of operating hours is small. Energy losses are usually quite high, unless there is further progress in battery technology.

Transportation

Transmitting power over long distances via high-voltage grids is expensive, especially if it requires large new investments. Networks cannot be used for storage, only for exporting excess electricity to other regions, or for importing. Networks are particularly expensive when they are only used a few hours per year. Not to forget, electricity gets lost when it is transported, proportionally to the distance.

New wide power corridors don't really create value. To explain, take the example of conventional motorways: if they were designed to permit every truck and every Porsche to be driven at full speed on a Friday afternoon before a holiday weekend, you would probably end up with ten-lane roads. Good for Porsche drivers, bad for the environment and simply unaffordable for the taxpayer, or whoever has to pay the bill. Normally two or three lanes are sufficient. That should be the basis for planning the motorways—not the requirement that everyone should be able to drive at top speed all the time.

Unfortunately, that is exactly what is happening right now in energy policy. The planned expansion of the grid is not consistent with the goals of the Energiewende but rather with those of the large utilities—their aim is to keep their coal-burning power plants running as long as possible. The new power highways would only make sense if energy from renewables and excess electricity from coal plants had to be transported to the south of Germany.

Weather

It is well known that high-pressure conditions or low-pressure areas with no sun can sometimes dominate the weather in Germany, but it is extremely rare that the entire country experiences exactly the same weather. For example, in the 800 hours per year when there is almost no wind near the North Sea, the probability that the south of the Black Forest will experience strong winds is 80 per cent. In addition, it is about time that we expand our policy horizon to include the entire European Union—there the weather differences are even larger than inside Germany.

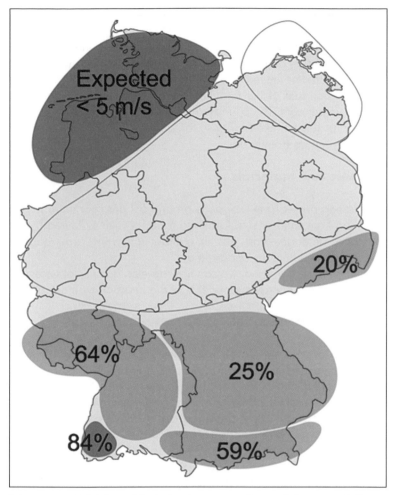

Below-average winds in the north (under 5 meters per second) can easily be compensated by good wind speeds in southern Germany.

Availability of renewable power

Wind and solar power is available everywhere in Germany. The potential for the generation of electricity is many times larger than present and future demand. Electricity from wind and solar power is the cheapest option, now and in eternity. That is why wind and photovoltaic power should provide the basic supply of electricity, not brown coal.

Hydroelectricity

Large hydroelectric stations can generate power at the same price as wind and sun, and sometimes for even less, but in Germany the potential is rather limited. Electricity from water currently accounts for three per cent of the total; its share can at most be raised to about five per cent. The country does not have the right geological conditions. It is not like Norway, for instance, where nearly all the electricity comes from water.

Organic raw materials

Generating power from biogas is around 50 per cent more expensive than from wind or sun. Growing food for fuels is limited by the available acreage—and it is in competition with crops that are needed to feed humans and animals.

With these aspects in mind, we can now develop an optimal system for the future of our energy supply. It is at the heart of my master plan.

The economic essentials of using wind and sun

We have a problem—fossil fuels are finite; betting on them is short-sighted and a poor allocation of capital. We also have a remedy—wind and solar energy. Now we need to define what this means in real life. How can we mix power from wind and sun in an optimal way? One condition is that the economy does not suffer. Better still, how can it be stimulated by switching to renewables? Is it possible to reduce the costs for the government and the public?

Here is the magic formula: energy supply based on wind and sun should be produced close to where it is consumed. This could actually be the motto of this book. Such a strategy avoids or minimizes storage and transportation costs and does not need much back-up from bioenergy. This can be achieved by spreading wind and solar power stations evenly throughout Germany and by identifying locations where the wind is strongest—provided that the wind parks do not violate nature conservation laws. If we follow the suggestions of the master plan, we won't need many more than those nearly 25,000 wind mills that exist already. We must also try to make sure that the electricity produced by wind and solar systems is fed into the grid as steadily as possible. To achieve this, it is important that the wind mills run more or less all the time at full load. We should aim for at least 4,000 full load hours per year, ie, twice as much as we get today. We also need more installations at exposed locations and on the coast. For solar power systems, the goal is to get from currently 1,000 full load hours to 1,500 to 2,000. It is possible.

Technological development of wind mills

Typical wind turbine in 2000	in 2010	in 2014
– 65 m hub height	– 100 m hub height	– 150 m hub height
– 75 m rotor	– 100 m rotor	– 120 m rotor
– 1,5 MW output	– 3 MWoutput	– 2.0–2.5 MW output
→ 1,500 full load hours	→ 2,500 full load hours	→ 4,000 full load hours

Over the past few years, wind mill technology has made an enormous leap forward—the wind mills have become much more productive. There is no end in sight.
Source: Calculations and images by "100 prozent erneuerbar stiftung"

What are full load hours and why are 4,000 to 5,000 hours the economic optimum for wind mills?

When I was writing this book, people warned me repeatedly not to get too technical. I'll try my best. Being a physicist, I know it's easier for me than for others to understand certain technical concepts. On the other hand, I am not good at foreign languages or music. Interestingly enough, when I say that I'm a physicist, the most common reaction is "Oh, I dropped that subject in tenth grade!"

Nonetheless, let me give you at this point an in-depth explanation of the term "full load hours". Once the term is fully understood, many other concepts can easily be understood as well. I have also noticed that the term is frequently used by lots of people, but I often have the feeling that some of them don't have an idea of what it actually means. I am explaining this concept to improve the understanding—in particular, I have in mind those who make the decisions about the structure of our future energy supply.

Okay, so what exactly are these ominous full load hours?

Let me use a farming analogy to explain the difference between energy and power. Let's assume that a farmer has a horse, a plow and a large field. A horse working at full capacity is equivalent to one horsepower (1 hp ≈ 0.74 kilowatts). If it does, the farmer needs around 10 hours to plow the field. The power (of the horse) is thus 1 hp (0.74 kW), the work performed (= energy) is 10 hph (10 hours × 1 hp). The number of full load hours (of the power plant called "horse") is therefore the amount of energy (10 hph) divided by 1 hp, ie, ten hours.

Now assume that the horse can only work at half its power (0.5 hp), perhaps because it has to carry some extra burden. In ten hours, the amount of work (= energy) would only be 0.5 times 10, or 5 hph. That means the horse would plow only half the field. And the number of full load hours? It would be 5 hph (amount of energy) divided by 1 hp (maximum power), ie, only five full load hours, even though the horse has worked for ten hours.

I hope that the term "full load hours" has become a bit clearer. In power plant and energy technology, the number of full load hours has become a key statistic for comparing technologies and locations. For years I have heard the argument that wind power is not efficient enough because the number of full load hours is significantly lower than that of conventional power plants.

This comparison is not acceptable: full load hours are not the right statistic for comparing the yield of wind mills with that of conventional power plants. Coal power plants can usually be run almost around the clock at full capacity and thus achieve a high number of full load hours: one can always add more coal to raise the power level. Wind energy and solar power systems are different because the "fuels" are wind and sunshine—whose inputs vary. But they are free. That's why the main issue is how much of the input of renewables can be transformed into electricity, not how intensively the generator is utilized. The task is to determine the number of full load hours that is best for our future system based on renewables.

But is it possible to run the generator of a wind mill at full capacity all the time, or most of the time?

YES, it is possible—technologically it's actually rather easy, even at inland locations with average or modest wind speeds. One has to combine a very small generator—for example one with 100 hp (74 kW), like the engine of a medium-sized car—with a very large rotor, for instance with a diameter of 120 meters. Even a mild breeze is enough to run the generator at full capacity. Around 7,500 to 8,000 hours a year at full load are realistic! As the reader knows by now, there are 8,760 hours in a year. From an engineering point of view, it would be ideal if the wind mill produced the same amount of electricity day after day, just like a conventional power plant.

So why isn't it done?

The amount of electricity produced by a wind wheel depends first of all on the velocity of the wind, but also on the surface that catches the wind, ie, the diameter of the rotor. It is less dependent on the power of the generator.

If the (small) generator was running at its maximum capacity all the time, we couldn't benefit from stronger winds: the generator would be cut off too early. Energy that is theoretically available would be wasted. The yield of the wind mill would then be too low relative to its construction cost.

It is actually possible to produce much more power by combining a large rotor, for instance 120 meters, with a large generator. When winds are strong, significantly more electricity can be produced than with a small generator. The downside: installing a large generator reduces the number of full load hours. In the past, 2,000 to 2,500 full load hours were the standard at many locations—and it still is standard today: large rotors and large generators.

When the wind is very strong, more electricity is produced and has to be fed into the grid. This requires a massive expansion of both the electricity grid and storage facilities. But what makes sense on a micro level is not the best solution from a macroeconomic perspective—after taking into account all costs.

The goal is therefore to find the right mix of maximum yield and maximum utilization, of creating a steady flow of electricity into the grid on the one hand and generating as much electricity as possible per unit of invested capital. The optimal number of full load hours is a compromise between the profitability of a wind mill and technical requirements. To provide a steady flow of electricity into the grid, the optimum is around 4,000 to 5,000 full load hours—4,000 at average inland locations and 5,000 at locations with high wind speeds.

This is plausible: at 7,000 to 8,000 full load hours per year, the cost of electricity from wind would multiply. In the range 4,000 to 5,000 hours, the costs only increase by a few per cent because it is not necessary to install a larger generator, a more resilient design of the system and an expensive connection to the grid; on the other hand, the production of electricity must be capped off only a few hundred hours each year.

Until now, wind mills have only been viewed one by one. In the initial phase of the Energiewende, it had not been necessary to analyze the system of wind mills as a whole. But now we are aiming for an exclusive supply of electricity from renewables. The rules of the game have therefore changed. The interactions have to be taken into account.

The change of the system means that around 60 per cent of Germany's electricity demand can be covered by wind mills, without a significant increase of the number of sites—and without raising electricity output much beyond demand when wind speeds are unusually high. I suggest that we can generate six times more electricity from wind with the same number of wind wheels!!

This is an important result for nature conservationists and for the protection of the landscape and the environment.

There is no lack of advanced technologies and space for a success of the Energiewende.

Wind mills in Germany

	End of 2012	Future (previous assumption)	Future (intelligent)
Wind turbines	23,000	**40,000**	25,000
Total output	31,000 MW	160,000 MW	80,000 MW
Average size	1,350 kW	3–5,000 kW	2–4,000 kW
Full load hours	2,000 h	2,000 h	4,000 h
Energy yield (Average year)	62 TWh	320 TWh	320 TWh
Percentage of electricity demand (540 TWh)	10%	60%	60%

Development of wind turbines: today vs. future vs. "intelligent" future

Full load hours of solar modules can also be increased, from 1,000 to between 1,500 and 2,000 a year. For this, the relationship between the size of the module and the size of the inverter must be adjusted.

Solar modules produce direct current (DC) and need inverters to turn it into alternating current (AC), the kind of electricity that is needed by consumers. Today, the modules and inverters of a solar system generally have the same power. As in the case of wind mill technology, solar power systems only reach maximum output when conditions are perfect—this does not happen very often.

For this reason, future inverters can be much smaller. At the same time, the yield of the modules should be increased. Expanding the surface area that is exposed to sunlight also raises the utilization rate of the inverter. This significantly boosts electricity production on cloudy days and in winter. When more solar energy is generated than the inverter can process, the excess is stored in batteries. When these are full, the electricity is turned into heat (primarily warm water), using buffer storage.

What do we do when there is no wind, or when the wind is too strong?

For nearly two decades, skeptics have asked me "what do we do when there is no wind and the sun isn't shining?" More recently, I often had to answer an additional question "what do we do when the wind is too strong or when there's too much sun?"

These are indeed the key questions. Following are my answers. Two fundamental strategies must be pursued for a successful Energiewende: 1. the three major forms of energy—electricity, heat and mobility—must be seen in combination, and 2. energy has to be used more efficiently than today.

This is what we do when there is too much wind

Here is the simplest and most cost-effective solution when there is too much wind or sun: **adjust energy consumption to match energy production.**

Put differently: when we generate "too much" electricity we use more of it than normal. But it is not wasted. We make provisions for periods when electricity production from renewables is not sufficient. As an example: on hot summer days with lots of sun we can use surplus electricity for cooling.

To adjust our electricity consumption when there is too much wind generally does not cost anything, or just a little. One inexpensive solution is to turn the current into heat in a power-to-heat system. Heat storage systems such as water tanks are relatively cheap; you find them in neighborhood heating networks and private households. When we have excess electricity, it can easily and quickly be transformed into heat using a simple device called immersion heater. In this way consumers can reduce their heating bills. Currently, the main heating fuels are oil and natural gas. In the future these will be replaced by biogas and wood pellets. Oil costs somewhat less than 10 euro cents per kilowatt hour—wind power is already a cheaper source of energy.

The second possibility is storage, combined with the above solutions for "too much" and "too little" electricity.

This is what we do when there is not enough wind

By producing electricity the way described above, wind, solar and hydropower will always make a contribution to overall electricity generation in Germany. But there will be times when this is not enough. For these periods we need combined (micro) heat and power units (CHPs), batteries or pumping plants with reservoirs. These are the essential elements of an electricity supply system that is tailored to the needs of consumers.

Pumping plants and batteries are important, but they can only be used to bridge small shortfalls: they cannot store much energy. They are ideal for using solar electricity at night or when, for example, everyone opens their refrigerator at the same time, as during the fifteen minute break between the first and second half of an international soccer match.

Pumping plants are of interest because there are already a number of them in Germany. They have a capacity of nearly 8,000 megawatts, which is about ten per cent of the maximum electricity consumption at any one time. More such facilities may be built but they will have to compete with modern batteries. These will be located closer to the consumer and are able to release nearly 100 per cent of the energy that they have taken in.

Battery storage units are used in private households, but mostly in commerce and industry. Synergies with today's "uninterruptible power supply" (UPS) technology are possible, such as battery back-up systems for supercomputers. In the future, millions of car batteries will be available—so many actually that only a small percentage of them will be needed for storing surplus electricity.

When we have less wind and solar power in winter, energy must be taken from other sources, primarily biomass or wind gas. For this we need **combined heat and power units (CHPs).**

Wind gas is hydrogen generated by electrolysis. It can be stored using the existing infrastructure for biogas. The capacity of the storage facilities is huge. The gas from underground gas caverns is enough to cover Germany's power demand for over 100 days! Via existing pipelines the gas can also be cheaply transported over long distances. The downside: only one third of the stored gas can be turned back into electricity. The rest must be burned to generate heat. This technology is most efficiently deployed in industry. To have enough electricity at all times, the number of CHPs must be significantly increased. They will mostly be installed by industry and local utilities. This is a mature technology. For many decades CHPs have proven their operational reliability. A CHP is essentially an engine that drives an electricity generator. It can be used flexibly at any time, comes in all sizes and is highly efficient.

Energy efficiency is essential for the energy system of the future

All raw materials and most of the stored energy must be used more efficiently. The savings potential is enormous. At the moment, much of our technology is extremely inefficient; this includes car engines, power stations and many biogas plants. Around 60 to 70 per cent of our energy is wasted and blown into the atmosphere. Efficient CHPs, located close to consumers, do virtually not lose any electricity or heat. And they are cheap.
The money that is planned to be spent on large overland grids—20 billion euros—would be enough to install CHPs with a total capacity of 40,000 to 50,000 megawatt. If the German government would take this sort of money to subsidize CHPs in business, the resulting reduction of energy costs would become a major advantage in terms of international competitiveness.
If the CHPs are so simple, reliable and efficient, why don't we use them on a large scale? Because they produce electricity by burning fuels, and these cost money. Sun, wind and water are much cheaper sources of energy. That is why I propose to use electricity from CHPs just for filling supply gaps.

What we will not do under any circumstance

As part of its Energiewende strategy, the previous CDU/CSU/FDP coalition government had planned to use night storage heaters to store wind and solar energy. It had lifted the predecessor government's ban on night storage heating that was going into effect in 2019. The reasoning makes sense: to provide incentives to consume energy when there is an oversupply in the grid, and to treat heat as a form of energy consumption.

Night storage heating was originally encouraged in order to store as much energy from nuclear power plants as possible. This meant that these could run at full capacity throughout the night. Wouldn't it be a good thing, then, to feed electric heating systems with excess electricity produced by renewables?

It sounds good, but in fact it's a bad idea.

Electric heating and heat pumps are counterproductive because they don't use the excess electricity from renewables. They require the installation of additional capacities to back up the system at the wrong time—in winter. Ten million households heating with electricity need an additional backup capacity of 200,000 megawatt. This is two to three times more than the capacity available today, and therefore not possible. The time of year when people have to heat their homes is when solar and wind energy is scarce in most parts of Germany. It is the time when the CHPs should be running at full capacity.

This means the previous (CDU/CSU/FDP) government had passed a law that doesn't take advantage of the excess production of electricity from wind and sun. It created a new, completely unnecessary power gap in the winter. Why?

Let's ask who benefits from this law and who lobbied for it in the first place. The answer: RWE, one of the four large utilities. Why? The company hopes to sell the electricity it generates by burning coal, even though there are much better solutions for consumers. CO_2-emissions would be ten times as high as those from normal condensing boilers.

The Energiewende is not about maximizing energy production by promoting inefficient systems. The idea is rather to reduce energy consumption as much as possible. To make the Energiewende as inexpensive for society as possible, we should ban all electric heating immediately and reduce the required backup capacities.

How should we use bioenergy?

Bioenergy has a reputation problem. It's said that it feeds cars instead of people (in German the slogan is "Teller oder Tank?"). It is important to know that only around 20 per cent of Germany's arable land is used to grow renewables. In 2001, 1.15 million hectares were used to grow biodiesel—mainly rapeseed –, and another 0.9 million hectares were for biogas—mostly corn. I am in favor of switching between different kinds of crops, to diversify and to avoid a monoculture, for instance one that is based on corn (maize).

To a large extent, world hunger is caused by meat production. Meat is a waste of calories, water, and energy as well as of arable land. It takes a lot of fodder to bring one kilogram of meat to the market. If we used the land to feed people instead of animals, we would go a long way to end world hunger. I don't want to convince anyone to become a vegetarian, but I think it's not unreasonable to ask people to control their meat consumption, to eat less of it.

Bioenergy will no longer be used to power automobiles

In the future, bioenergy must be used more efficiently. Burning it as fuel in conventional cars is highly inefficient. It makes more sense to use it as an input in CHPs which simultaneously generate electricity and heat. Large CHPs can be found at local utilities, in factories and office buildings that need both electricity and heat. Micro CHPs are mostly for private households. They are highly efficient, transportation losses are small, and they don't need much storage space. We have lots of capacity: at over one million hectares, the space that we currently require for biofuel is much larger than the area for growing biogas crops.

Biogas will be burned more quickly and more efficiently

Bioenergy plants currently run almost 24 hours a day, which gives them about 8,000 full load hours a year which is comparable to the utilization rate of power stations that burn brown coal. But when wind and solar energy is available, we don't need expensive bioenergy. Rather than producing and using bioenergy at a constant rate throughout the year, it makes more sense to save it as a backup for the days when wind and sun are not available. In other words, we need 2,000 full capacity hours instead of 8,000.

Biogas can easily be stored in caverns. If it is used up in a short period of time instead of bit by bit, it is possible to increase power significantly. Presently, bioenergy generated from just over two million hectares can compensate for the average annual shortfall caused by the days when there is not enough wind and sun. The backup will usually be needed during the winter when, for example, wind parks are operating at only 15 per cent of capacity.

We don't need any more space for bioenergy

Raising energy efficiency will allow us to switch to 100 per cent renewable energy without expanding the acreage devoted to bioenergy. In our calculations, we have actually not taken into account that the efficiency of biogas plants can probably be improved considerably. Moreover, I expect that scientific progress will continue to raise the harvested amount of energy raw materials per hectare. Further improvements in the biological transformation process will one day yield 50 to 100 per cent more energy from the crops. In the final analysis, bioenergy has to compete with wind gas. Hard to say which technology will prevail in the long run—the one that makes most economic sense will win.

The formula of the master plan: 60 + 25 + 5

It is theoretically as well as in real life possible to achieve a constant flow of energy from wind and sun. We need systems that can catch a lot of wind and a lot of sun, and are equipped with small generators and small inverter modules, respectively. These systems must produce electricity at lots of locations all across Germany, wherever the conditions are good—but always close to the consumer.

We can cover around 60 per cent of our energy needs with wind power, and around 25 per cent with solar power. Another 5 per cent will come from hydro-electric power plants. The rest will be supplied by CHPs that use bioenergy.

On a warm summer day, Germans consume 40,000 megawatt of energy; at peak times, for example on cold winter afternoons, they use up to 80,000 megawatt. The last number is also the maximum amount that can be fed into the grid. If electricity generation is decentralized and close to where the demand is, it is possible to integrate 80,000 megawatt of wind power into the power grid.

Once wind mills have been optimized to run for 4,000 full load hours a year, they will be able to provide up to 320 terawatt hours. Germany's net energy consumption is currently approximately 540 terawatt hours. In the future, 25,000 modern wind mills can thus generate 60 per cent of the net energy demand.

Why 25 per cent from solar power?

It can be done by optimizing our use of solar energy. It means increasing the number of full load hours to 1,500 to 2,000, and boosting the yield of rooftop systems. In this way, yields can also be raised significantly on cloudy days, and in winter in particular. The excess power will be stored—primarily in batteries—and turned into heat, mainly warm water. Compared to all scenarios that have been presented to the public so far, we need much less long-term power storage. The trick is to generate most of the energy directly, using wind and sun, and to do it close to where the demand is.

The second formula of the master plan: energy + heat + mobility + efficiency

The master plan is comprehensive. It brings together three markets: electricity, heating and fuel for mobility. Given that oil prices keep rising and that we are running out of reserves, it's clear that we have to act quickly to change engines and mobility from hydrocarbons to renewables. The additional electricity for electro-mobility will be made available by wasting less energy, for example by banning standby functions in electronic devices, or by increasing efficiency elsewhere. Overall energy consumption can be kept unchanged this way. An optimal combination of the three energy markets together with a more efficient use of energy is the recipe for the future.

Energy autarky in all areas of consumption is a realistic goal—from private homes to industry. It requires the combination of wind and solar power generation, maximizing the number of full load hours plus CHP units that run on bioenergy.

If the master plan is skillfully implemented, efficiency gains will reduce our primary energy consumption by 25 per cent. Primary energy (eg, coal) is used to generate end-use energy (eg, electricity). If my concept is implemented, we will never pay more than 10 cents per kilowatt hour of electricity. That means we spend less on energy than we pay for imported hydrocarbons today. The savings are more than sufficient to finance the introduction of electro-mobility and the insulation of our houses.

Three myths disproved by the master plan

Myth number 1: wind and solar power won't work because it is not possible to provide stable voltage and frequencies

Wrong. For a smooth operation of the grid, the voltage should not fluctuate while the grid frequency must remain constant at 50 Hz. In this regard, modern wind and solar power systems have the same characteristics as conventional power stations. CHPs can be connected to, or disconnected from the grid, turned up or down as needed in order to ensure that stability.

The future storage capacity of batteries will be several times larger than our maximum energy demand today. The one million electric cars—which the German government wants to have on the road by 2020—would already be sufficient.

But the car batteries won't be connected to the grid at the same time, right? No, they won't. But once there are perhaps 30 to

40 million electric cars, with an average usage time of half an hour a day, there will always be enough vehicles connected to the grid.

Myth number 2: we need offshore wind mills to guarantee a sufficient number of full load hours and to create jobs

Wrong. The master plan is very clear on one issue: we definitely cannot afford offshore wind mills. The arguments for offshore wind power have always been the high number of full load hours, the lack of space inland and the lower cost. All of these have been disproved. Wind mills in the North Sea and the Baltic Sea would be too far away from consumers and require huge and expensive grids as well as larger storage capacities. Revenues would go to the big players rather than to energy cooperatives and local people.

It's true that offshore wind wheels have a high number of full load hours. I argue that significantly more full load hours are possible onshore than is usually assumed. The trick is to use the right wind mill technology and combine it with solar power in-stallations.

Due to innovations and the mass production of solar modules, solar energy has become far cheaper than offshore wind energy. Offshore installations are about to become the most expensive way to produce electricity. It is already more than two to three times more expensive than wind energy onshore.

I've talked about this with a number of politicians—with Peter Altmaier, the previous environment minister, as well as with members of the SPD and the Green Party. They all agreed but usually added that offshore wind parks would create a lot of jobs. This is like saying "let people dig holes in the ground and then fill them again—it creates jobs", even though this is total nonsense and a waste of resources. Moreover, in 2012, the solar industry created six times as many jobs as the offshore industry, despite the fact that politicians had drastically cut feed-in tariffs (because electricity had become too expensive for consumers).

I don't see why the cost argument should not be applied to the most expensive method of generating electricity. The point is that the producers of offshore electricity are the large utilities. Once you are aware of this, it will not surprise you that the federal parliament in Berlin—the Bundestag—has recently decided to subsidize offshore wind energy, at the height of the debate over electricity prices. It didn't seem to matter that there was no grid to transmit this additional power.

Myth number 3: we have to expand the grid

Also wrong. All studies that support grid expansion make the erroneous claim that future wind mills will only achieve 2,000 to 2,500 full load hours. The analysts either don't know that the number of full load hours can easily be adjusted, or they are aiming to feed as much wind and solar power into the grid as possible, but also electricity from coal.

As I said before: expanding the grid follows the same logic as creating a ten-lane highway so that all Porsches can at any time be driven at full speed, without taking into account the economic and environmental costs.

I guess that electricity from coal is important for the earnings of the big utilities. Members of Angela Merkel's government may want to support these firms and simply do not know better. At any rate, they have consistently supported a quick and comprehensive expansion of the grid. This is also about outsmarting the Greens, getting them caught between their two main interests—the Energiewende (more energy from renewables) and the protection of the environment.

Since we do not need offshore energy, as I have shown earlier, we also don't need to expand the grid to the highest possible voltage level. What we need is wind mills all across the country, and close to consumers. There are simple ways to turn excess electricity into heat or gas and store it. Investment expenditures would be less than the money needed for the proposed grid expansion. But old wind mills with sub-optimal full load hours must be replaced by more efficient ones.

What does the master plan mean for normal people?

In my master plan, electricity is not considered on its own, but rather as part of an overall system of energy supply—in combination with heating and mobility. The average German household spends 5,000 euros annually for this energy package. Politicians and the public are agitated about the 200 euro EEG-levy but ignore the other 4,800 euros. They are also not talking about the risk that fossil fuels may become considerably more expensive and that it is strategically important to reduce our dependence on them, especially on imported oil and gas.

Former environment minister Peter Altmaier visiting the juwi headquarters in the summer of 2012

That is why it's time we finally start to name the people who are truly driving up energy costs—and fight them. We have to do it together, ideally with the support of Sigmar Gabriel who is now responsible for the energy portfolio in Berlin. That is why I want to address him directly: "Dear vice chancellor Gabriel, we do not need an electricity price brake that will result in higher electricity prices long-term. What we need is a reduced EEG-levy for low-income households.
We need to stop subsidizing conventional energy.
We need to control the price setting policies of the electricity and oil cartels.

Every year we spend 200 billion euros on energy, 7 per cent of GDP, and the trend is still strongly up.
We need to hit the brakes, vice chancellor.
We shouldn't invest in yesterday's technologies and systems.
And we need to start by immediately switching to 100 per cent renewable energies.
If anyone is able to do this, it is you."
The government must now identify the best locations for wind mills, while at the same time keeping an eye on the quality of the environment. The revised EEG-law must provide the framework for the reforms I am proposing in this book. These should not be put on hold.

The master plan for energy, heat and mobility

This is how we can quickly achieve an energy supply based entirely on renewable energies:

1. The formula of the master plan is: 60 per cent wind, 25 per cent solar, 5 per cent hydroelectricity. The rest comes from CHPs (combined heat and power units) that run on bioenergy.

2. We will primarily rely on wind and solar energy—the supply of wind and sunshine is unlimited, and it does not cost anything. This will end our dependence on expensive imports and rising prices of oil, coal and gas.

3. Wind and solar energy can provide a reliable electricity supply around the clock. Winter power gaps can be filled by bioenergy and stored electricity.

4. The power generating systems will be designed to provide as much electricity as possible, and in a steady way. We try to distribute the energy systems evenly throughout Germany at locations with the greatest potential yield. We will select the technology best suited at these locations.

5. We do not need more wind mills than we already have, nor any additional land for bioenergy. We will not use high-voltage lines or expensive offshore systems, and we will make it easier to store electricity.

6. Our energy supply will not only be completely clean and sustainable, but also reliable and affordable in the long term.

7. By using electricity, heat and mobility more efficiently, we will be able to produce energy at lower prices than we are currently paying for imported hydrocarbons, not just in the distant future but very soon. With the money we save, we can switch to electric cars and insulate our homes.

Afterword: Dear chancellor, please keep in mind the future of the world's society!

This book cannot provide all solutions. That would be too ambitious. My master plan is a blueprint for the future, based on a sober look at the situation today. I argue that the one hundred per cent switch to renewable energies has positive effects on the social, economic, ecological and democratic fabric of our society.

The German government still believes that we can achieve the Energiewende in cooperation with the large utilities. That is a fundamental mistake. A true decentralized transition to renewable energy is not possible without the involvement of citizens. Other important players are energy cooperatives, local governments and municipal utilities. We are dealing with a fundamental transformation of the system— from a few large companies to millions of electricity producers.

A future based on renewable energies will save us a lot of money. To be sure, the Energiewende is not just about switching to new inputs— wind, sun, water and biomass—and about making us independent of directly and indirectly subsidized nuclear and fossil fuels. We must no longer rely on a few large utilities. We introduce democratic processes in the organization of electricity production and gain an additional degree of freedom this way. The Energiewende is also about the protection of the environment and thus about the future of our children—and the earth. It will also change the lives of the world's poor who do not have access to electricity today.

This is what is motivating me.

The skeptics agree that the Energiewende is a worthy cause but doubt that it can be achieved quickly. That is wrong. It can be brought about in a very short time. We can achieve the 100 per cent goal in six years. We can also construct storage facilities in six years. Peter Altmaier, the former minister for the environment, saw things the same way when he came to our Wörrstadt headquarters in August 2012.

At some point during the discussion, I told him that "the government's goal of 35 per cent by 2020 is no problem at all."

He admitted that "from a purely technical perspective, we can indeed achieve 100 per cent by 2020."

Exactly. Why should we postpone the solution of mankind's largest problem? Why actually aggravate the problem by building new coal-burning power plants? We can solve it here and now. Procrastination is bad politics.

Instead of 80 per cent renewables by 2050, I prefer 100 per cent by 2020.

If we focus on evenly spreading the construction of solar and wind energy sites across the country, close to existing grids and consumers, we save a lot of resources: no high-voltage grid expansion, less spending on storage, no additional use of land. And, most importantly, sunshine and wind do not cost anything; they are available everywhere.

When the wind does not blow on a cloudy winter day, we switch to bioenergy, hydropower and local storage.

Dear Ms. Merkel, when I tried to talk to you about the implementation of the Energiewende—you may remember our return flight from Chile—you didn't have time but asked me to write you a letter instead. I felt I had been brushed off at the time and was frustrated. But thinking about it, I decided to write down what I would have loved to discuss with you during the flight. As you can see, it has become a book. I hope it finds a broad audience, but I have mostly written it for you.

What can be more satisfying for a politician than to undo undesirable economic, social and environmental developments and to lead the way to an affordable and independent energy future?

So please, accept my offer: I will donate the shares in my company to Germany's energy cooperatives in exchange for a swift 100 per cent Energiewende. Ethically and economically it is the best offer you can get. I will also give the royalties of this book to "Die Bürgerenergiewende" campaign.

I am aware that critics and skeptics will attack me, accuse me of self-interest and try to refute my conclusions on the basis of other data—and thus discredit me. That is a risk I am willing to take.

And yes, there are a few firms which will lose money if the energy market is reformed along the lines that I have described in this book. On the other hand, most people will benefit a lot, in Germany, worldwide and for generations to come.

And you will go down in history—as the chancellor who gave the world a future.

Ms. Chancellor, give our earth the air to breathe!

Acknowledgements

This is my first book. How can I say thank you to all the people who helped me on my way, and to the many readers who gave me their precious time to learn about the essentials of the Energiewende? I hope I could convince them that I am fighting a worthwhile fight. I also hope they will join me.

Those who do not take the first step will never reach the finish line. Faithful to this motto, I have written almost 150 pages in a few weeks. I have corrected, edited, rephrased and worked straight through many nights.

Yet I still needed the advice, assistance and support of friends, colleagues and employees. I thank all of you from the bottom of my heart.

I thank my juwi Corporate Communications Team, Christian Hinsch and Michael Löhr, for inspiration and critical monitoring. I especially want to thank Ricarda Schuller who was a great assistant during the entire project, and also Valerie Speth for providing and checking the facts and figures.

Dieter Wermuth, economist and partner of the Mainz-based Wermuth Asset Management GmbH had the idea to translate my original German book into English, add some new charts and update the text, especially with regard to the political changes after the September 22, 2013 federal elections. Germany is now governed by a grand coalition under Ms Merkel—it has an 80 per cent majority in the Bundestag and could easily accelerate the Energiewende. Dieter spent several hundred hours on this project, free of charge. He is convinced that my book deserves a broad international audience. I am quite grateful.

And last but not least, I bow to those whose names I cannot mention here. Without their help, the first (German) edition would not have become such a bestselling book.

The Energiewende—four outside views

"The transition towards a decentralized energy supply with renewable energies offers great potential, especially for rural areas. We have to use this opportunity locally and in the region. Moreover, the process needs to be accelerated. I am optimistic that we can achieve the energy transition if we continue to follow the chosen path consequently and without watering down the objectives. The world is watching us. Therefore, the energy transition must not fail."
Markus Conrad (CDU), mayor of the Wörrstadt municipality

"Mr. 100%. I first met Matthias Willenbacher a couple of years ago at a gala evening. He was honored with the Green-Tech award for his great contribution to the protection of the environment. At that event, he presented his idea of an energy supply based on 100 per cent renewables. His enthusiasm immediately inspired the audience. Everyone in the hall was convinced that things can be changed for the better. All it takes is someone who is able to explain the broader context of the German Energiewende in an objective and understandable manner. His book explains why we can completely withdraw from nuclear power in a short time and why an energy supply based on renewables is the way to go.
Dear Mrs. Merkel, after having read Matthias Willenbacher's indecent proposal to you, I wish he's able to seduce you—for the benefit of my children, my family and all living creatures. I am convinced, you are satisfied afterwards ☺"
Tina Ruland, actress, Berlin

"Cooperatives are the basis of the German Energiewende because everyone is able to participate, even without much money. In our cooperative, shares are already available for 500 euros. We don't want big investors in our cooperative, that's why there's a limit for investments. Actually, the energy transition should be realized locally and in a decentralized way because that is the true nature of renewables. Their great advantage: they produce energy where it is needed the most – close to the consumer. Instead, our government promotes the industrial-scale approach and further supports centralized structures."
Joachim Thees, CEO of BürgerEnergie Tauberfranken

"The Bürgerenergiewende, energy production based on renewables and the involvement of the citizens, is the economically most viable approach. It is the only way of keeping profits in our region. Locally, we are thus able to demonstrate that climate protection, a reliable and socially acceptable energy supply as well as sustainable investments can be compatible. We must not miss this chance."
Kai Hock, founder and CEO of HEG Heidelberger Energiegenossenschaft eG.